IN SEARCH OF
TAYLOR CALDWELL

ALSO BY JESS STEARN

Edgar Cayce—The Sleeping Prophet

Yoga, Youth and Reincarnation

The Door to the Future

The Search for the Girl with the Blue Eyes

The Miracle Workers—America's Psychic Consultants

The Sixth Man

The Search for a Soul

Power of Alpha Thinking

IN SEARCH OF
TAYLOR CALDWELL

JESS STEARN

𝔰𝔇

STEIN AND DAY/Publishers/New York

First published in 1981
Copyright © 1981 by Jess Stearn
All rights reserved.
Designed by Judith E. Dalzell
Printed in the United States of America

STEIN AND DAY/*Publishers*
Scarborough House
Briarcliff Manor, N.Y. 10510

Library of Congress Cataloging in Publication Data
Stearn, Jess.
    In search of Taylor Caldwell.

1. Caldwell, Taylor, 1900-   —Biography.
2. Novelists, American—20th century—Biography.
I. Title.
PS3505.A364Z878   813'.52 [B]   80-6150
ISBN 0-8128-2791-0   AACR2

This book is dedicated to the millions of readers whose lives have been enriched by the wondrous imagination and memory of that most remarkable author—Taylor Caldwell

IN SEARCH OF
TAYLOR CALDWELL

Chapter One

ENTER THE STAR

THE telephone had an insistent ring, and I picked it up, little realizing the effect it would have on my life. The caller was Neltje Doubleday, of the Doubleday publishing family, and there was an uncertain quaver in her voice.

"I am having a little dinner for Taylor Caldwell," she said, "and I would like you to come."

I was not only surprised at this opportunity to meet so distinguished a novelist, but at Neltje's apparent nervousness.

"But why?" I said. "I never met the gentleman."

There was a pause, and then Neltje said with a sigh:

"Taylor is a woman. She wants to meet you. And I must tell you, she has whims of steel."

At this time, the Spring of 1962, I had no idea why this world-renowned author would wish to meet a neophyte like myself, but Neltje was strangely persistent. And now, as I look back some twenty years, I see that the meeting was inevitable, for future events have a curious way of shaping the present.

It was a small dinner indeed. As I entered Neltje's New York apartment, I saw a handful of people clustered about the fireplace. I immediately picked out Lee Barker and Ken Mc-Cormick, Doubleday's top editors, and Neltje's husband, John Sargent, president of Doubleday. There was another couple present, sitting by each other, and I assumed the woman was Taylor Caldwell. She was speaking volubly, in a commanding voice, but looked up at my entrance and gave me a searching glance.

Neltje lost no time in introducing us. The novelist, to my

surprise, stood up to take my hand and we again traded glances.

You could tell she was somebody, even if she had not been holding the center stage. She looked right at you and through you. Her eyes flashed over my face, summing me up in that instant. I tried to do as much, but she was a difficult study. It was hard to tell her age, for she had an indeterminate, timeless look, neither old nor young. She was formidable looking, with her bold features and darting birdlike eyes of uncertain color. She was more fascinating, perhaps, than attractive. Her face glowed with animation, and her vermilion lips appeared to match the necklace of rubies draped loosely around her neck. As she lifted her head, I was struck by the lean whiteness of her throat, which could have belonged to a woman of thirty. Her nose was aquiline, and with the flowing red mane of a lioness and a hearty laugh—which showed her strong white teeth—she had the unmistakable look of a buccaneer.

The chiseled chin bespoke determination, and I was sure she was used to her own way, unless it suited her otherwise.

She had been speaking brusquely, almost stridently, but now she was all sweetness.

"I'm Janet Reback," she smiled. "How good of you to come."

It was indicative of some facet of her personality, I suppose, that she chose to use her married name.

Her eyes moved over the small circle, and she nodded at a dark, square-jawed man sitting next to her. He glowered at me disagreeably.

"And this is my husband, Marcus Reback," she said. "Don't mind him. He looks at every man that way."

I was struck by the dazzling display of jewelry. In addition to the ruby necklace, she wore an emerald brooch, and her long shapely arms gleamed with a rare assortment of diamonds and rubies. I had never seen so much precious jewelry outside of a Fifth Avenue jewelry shop.

I caught her smile as our eyes met. It seemed to say, "You

and I have a lot to say to each other." And then her eyes slid over the others, who were politely chatting, as if to add, "All these are outsiders."

In a swift movement she hooked her arm through mine and gently but irresistibly drew me over to a corner of the room, by a large window from which the bright towers of Manhanttan could be seen arching high into the sky.

I saw the amused smiles, and Barker particularly appeared to savor my bewilderment. But as she stood by the window, peering down onto the rooftops far below, she appeared oblivious of the others, and her face, which was subject to dramatic changes, took on a melancholy aspect.

"You are one of the few," she said, "that knows what is coming. Those poor people," she went on, taking in New York's millions with a wave of her hand, "little do they know what is to befall them."

Even as I wondered why she had wanted to meet me, I felt myself almost hypnotized by the certainty in her voice.

"And what is this terrible catastrophe?"

Her eyes widened and she looked at me in amazement.

"You don't know, and yet you mention it in your book?"

I was a little startled, since *The Door to the Future*, my book on the mystical, to be published by Doubleday, had not yet gone to the printers.

Her voice dropped to a whisper.

"There is even a time for it," she said, "in your time if not mine. And the destruction will be worldwide. Your Edgar Cayce"—a mystic mentioned in my book—"foresaw the destruction of New York, California, and much of the country by 1998, and Nostradamus foresaw a calamitous attack on the earth from outer space in 1999. It will all come together by the end of the century."

I took these dire predictions with a grain of salt.

"A hundred years ago," I said, "proclaiming the end of the world, a sect known as the Millerites gave away their worldly possessions and bought ascension robes for the climb into heaven. They wound up trying to get their property back."

She had recently published the fabulously successful story of Luke, *Dear and Glorious Physician*, and was steeped in Biblical lore.

"It's all in Matthew," she said and proceeded to recite in a sepulchral tone from a section of the Bible I had used in my book.

"If a man is on the roof, he must not come down to fetch his goods from the house; if in the field, he must not turn back for his coat. Alas for women with child in those days, and for those who have children at the breast."

I was intrigued, not so much by what she was saying—I was quite familiar with this rollcall of doom—but by her interest and her including me in this interest.

She had no trouble reading my thoughts.

"You can't talk to just anybody about things like this. They'd put you in a padded cell."

Her eyes took on a distant look I was to know so well.

"That Day of Judgment is coming. A day when the multitude will no longer shrug or sneer, mind my words. And it is all in the Bible, which Christians, and Jews, too, in some respects, supposedly believe in. But of course they only believe what is expedient."

She turned the full force of her presence on me, her eyes delving into mine as she said solemnly: "Somebody must sound the warning, so the people will be ready."

I had my own thoughts about destiny and determinism, but out of curiosity inquired:

"And what is to save poor suffering humanity?"

She looked at me sharply to detect a sneer, then seemed reassured.

"Nothing, I suppose, because man is not bright enough to mend his ways. As it happened in the time of Lot and of Noah, so will it again. When the earth trembles and yawning caverns of fire rend its surface from the destructive weapons man has forged, it will be too late for repentance. But as Christ said, man must prepare himself—and we must help."

She caught my smile.

"Oh, I'm not your dumb psalm-singing evangelist trying to scare everybody to their knees, but obviously Matthew spoke of nuclear warfare and contamination not even touched on at Hiroshima."

She went on quoting from the Old and New Testaments. Her knowledge of the Bible was prodigious, but all of the same turn. My head was reeling with all this destruction, but I wondered, incongruously, about dinner, for it was getting late and, like most people, I shunned whatever was unpleasant that I could do nothing about.

Her eyes skimmed past me to the group by the fireplace, looking over at us occasionally, never dreaming, I was sure, of the nature of our conversation.

"There's no hurry," she said, "they're only on the second drink."

I could see Lee Barker glancing over, and Marcus Reback was fidgeting nervously, clearly more concerned with us than with the people he was chatting with. I saw Barker pat him on the shoulder, then stand up and come toward us. Janet hardly looked up at Barker's approach, and when he said something about dinner, she snorted disdainfully.

"Who cares about food?"

He laughed agreeably. "We do."

"Didn't Jesus say we should worry more about what came out of our mouth than what went into it?"

She showed no sign of getting back to the others, puffing one cigarette after another until the smoke burned my eyes and left me wondering whether it was worse to be stifled by smoke or incinerated by a nuclear bomb.

"What are you two talking about?" he demanded.

"Miss Caldwell," I said, "is predicting the end of the world."

She drew herself up in mock dismay.

"Not I," she said, "but the Prophets of old." Her voice fell to a whisper and she held up a hand as if hearkening to a secret voice.

"And the great city was divided into three parts, and the cities of the nations fell; and great Babylon came in remembrance before God, to give unto her the cup of the wine of the fierceness of his wrath.

"And every island fled away, and the mountains were not found."

In the uncertain pause, Lee Barker's sardonic features turned solemn.

"And Babylon?" I asked.

She gave me a piercing glance.

"Babylon is already doomed. What city do you make it?"

"New York, Los Angeles?"

"Others will say London or Paris, some Rome. It depends on which horns of the beast these kingdoms are perceived. But in one terrible hour of judgment, it will be laid to waste."

She was speaking of Revelation, of course, of Armageddon, and the promised struggle between good and evil. And she had already picked the loser.

Barker gave her an indulgent look.

"One hour?"

She shrugged her shoulders.

"What the Lord gives, he can take away in an instant. His message is clear. So far, and no further, my wicked, wicked children. And then He shall send Him who He sent once before. Let us hope that the few who are left shall listen."

Barker laughed heartily. "They should; they will have been scared almost to death by that time."

He was pointedly eyeing his watch.

"Now don't get fidgety, Lee," she said. "Lee knows how much there is to the psychic, and I've predicted a few things for him psychically."

"Janet," he said, "will you come to dinner?"

"Not," she rejoined, "until I make my point."

"And that is?"

"That we feel more than we know, and that the universe is especially receptive to this nonreasoning process. Children have a way of getting at the truth before scholars, because of the simplicity with which they look at things. Their minds aren't polluted with all this garbage that's gradually stuffed into them. They have a faculty of seeing the heart of things, of remembering with some sixth sense, until it's ridiculed out of them by superior adults."

Barker was accustomed to saying what he thought.

"That's nonsense, Janet," he said, "and you know it."

"I know nothing of the kind," she returned stiffly, "and when we're all blown up you'll know it." She smiled. "For shall not a small child lead them?"

Barker stood up and offered his arm. "Janet," he said firmly, "you're holding up the parade."

"All right," she said with feigned resignation.

And so arm in arm we marched in to dinner, without my having the slightest idea why she had wanted to meet me, or why she was so enthusiastically forecasting the end of the world.

Chapter Two

OF CABBAGES AND QUEENS

"My God," she said, noting it was noon, "it's the middle of the night."

She was giving one of her rare interviews, and the reporter, a young girl, glanced at her incredulously.

"You said you write all night?"

I have no set time," said Janet, giving the girl a pitying look. "That's for peasants. I might as well be working in a butcher shop. I prefer the nights because I feel alive at night, being a night person. There are no interruptions, no telephones, no doorbells."

She had invited me to her hotel the next day, saying she wanted to finish our conversation, and so I had not expected to find her occupied.

"Sit down, sit down," she had exclaimed. "We'll be through in a few minutes; they always ask the same questions." When the reporter stared at me, she introduced me in glowing terms. "This is a very famous journalist," she said, gilding the lily a bit. "He has won many prizes for reporting."

The girl gave me a look of suspicion, which I sought to turn away by shopping through a magazine or two while still listening to Janet describe her writing habits. Actually, she had no fixed program. "When I sit down to my electric typewriter, I do not stop until I have exhausted whatever thoughts occupied my subconscious mind.

"Sometimes I run on from eight at night to eight the next morning, clacking furiously at the typewriter. I don't belong to the school of 'One thousand words before breakfast, two thousand before lunch, and two thousand more by five o'clock.' That is mechanistic—and masochistic.

"I write until I run dry, then wait for the well to fill up again. It may take a few hours, a few days, or a few weeks, or longer. I have put some books aside for years."

She looked over to me with a smile, stifling a yawn. "It's not like being a journalist, where somebody is always giving you something to write about. What a blessing that would be."

She was a perfectionist of sorts. "I'm never through with a book, really. I read and reread the books I have written to see where I could have improved them, where I could have cut, or introduced another line of thought. This helps in future writing to avoid errors and redundancies."

She looked over at me amiably. "It also is tedious, as you well know."

She had one or two idiosyncrasies. She preferred white book covers, and titles with four words, which she considered lucky.

"You can use all the luck you can get," she said. "I sometimes think that's better than being smart."

Though she was responding to the girl's questions, I had the impression from the way she kept turning to me that her answers were framed for my benefit as well.

Almost disdainfully, she watched the girl scribbling furiously to get it all down. "Why don't you learn shorthand?" she said. "I did; it made a courthouse reporter out of me."

The girl blushed under her scrutinizing eye.

"It must be wonderful to write novels," she said. "I just loved your *Dynasty of Death* and *This Side of Innocence.*"

The author gave her a look of ineffable disgust.

"What is wonderful about it? It's damn hard work, sitting at a cold typewriter and trying to make it hot."

I was curious myself about how she worked, and pointed

out that a popular young writer of the day had said that he just slipped his pages out of the typewriter and dashed them off to his publisher without looking at them again.

Janet's eyes flashed with scorn.

"He's not a writer. He's a typist."

After typing fifteen or twenty pages, double-spaced, she went over them carefully, trimming and adding here and there, changing a word, doing whatever she could to point up her central theme.

"I never do anything but my best," she said. "And if I think it is not my best, it never gets to my editor. I feel," she said, with a glance for me, "that a novelist shouldn't permit his problems—sickness, domestic difficulties, deaths in the family—to interfere with his work. There's nothing more important than what he creates."

She was well aware that the critics considered her wordy, transient, at best a story-teller. But she didn't write for them. She had a million readers for every carping critic. Her new books brought huge advances, and her old ones were being reissued with payments larger than she had originally received. She had made millions without critical approval.

"There seems to be some idea," she said, "that if a novelist's books are widely read, then these books can't have much to say, hardly worth the while of serious reviewers who sell their free review copies by the pound-weight to the various book outlets, often without opening them."

The girl had put down her pencil and was staring at the author with her mouth hanging open.

"You mean this happens to your books?"

"All books," she said caustically. "As fast as they get them, and sometimes before they read them." She felt reviewers were in effect looking down at the reading public when they ridiculed their taste for popular fiction. She frowned for a moment. "If a book is not read generally, then it is a failure, no matter what your family, or some critic, thinks about it."

She had been chainsmoking through the interview, and

now she snuffed out her cigarette with a sigh and glanced at the wall clock. "Do you have what you want, little girl?"

The girl, fumbling with her notes, nodded uncertainly. "I think so, except . . . "

She suddenly flushed with embarrassment.

"Well, out with it," said the novelist, tempering her shortness with an encouraging smile.

The girl became even more flustered. "My editor," she finally blurted out, "said I should ask how much money you make."

Janet smacked her lips over her answer. "Enough so that the Infernal Revenue Service loves me."

She stood up, ending the interview.

"Thank you for coming," she said, smiling benignly, "but I really don't know why anybody wants to read about writers. They're so dull."

She turned graciously to me, softening her words.

"In any event," she said, "you're more of a newspaperman, and they live exciting lives."

We watched the door close on the girl.

"That poor girl," she said, "she should be home having babies."

I could see she was enjoying herself, obviously exploiting an opportunity to get off a few of her opinions. But, again, alone with me, I noticed an abrupt change in attitude, a considerateness I had not seen with others. And I felt most comfortable, sitting and talking with her, however barbed her comments. We seemed to have an instant rapport. I had never met anyone I felt so in touch with, and yet we were strangers. The others called her Janet. And she had introduced herself as Mrs. Reback. What should I call her?

"Janet, or Taylor Caldwell," she said crisply. "It's my name. It so happens I was baptized Janet Taylor Miriam Holland Caldwell in the New Burey Methodist Church in October 1900, in Preswich, Manchester, England."

The legendary Max Perkins of Scribners, her first publisher, had suggested the name.

"I never liked 'Janet,'" she said. "So I used my family names of Taylor and Caldwell on his advice. Later I wanted to use J. T. Caldwell. But as my first book *Dynasty of Death*, was a best-seller, and the name became known, I was stuck with Taylor.

"Actually," she chuckled, "coming from a ruggedly individualistic Scotch-English-Irish family, I was christened five times, first as a Methodist but lastly as a Catholic, which is what I am now."

She talked freely about herself now, as though she knew I wanted to know everything there was to know about her. She picked up on my questions before I could frame them. And she dug deeply into the past, from childhood on. She seemed strangely fascinated by her own childhood.

"I was quite a kid," she said.

When she was six, her father, Arthur, an artist with the *Manchester Guardian*, moved his wife, Anne; Janet and her brother, Arthur Jr., to Buffalo and another newspaper job. It had been a difficult adjustment. A day-dreaming Janet was thought odd by the other children, and they shunned her. She had no friends, nor did she care, for the other young people indulged in childish trivia while she moved in an imaginary world of storied palaces and strange people who whispered delightful secrets in her ear. School was a bore, but it was here she began writing down whatever wild thoughts raced through her mind. As a fifth-grader she pictured the lost continent of Atlantis in all its glory and decline, in a five-hundred page single-spaced manuscript, never having heard the name Atlantis before and not knowing why she even thought about it. She took her title from Ecclesiastes: *This Also Is Vanity.*

At nine she had produced another manuscript which she had slaved over secretly, not letting anyone see it for fear of ridicule. Then hearing that her idol, Mark Twain, was in Buffalo, she rushed over to the house he was stopping at. She saw the great man sauntering down the steps, his snow-white mane gleaming in the sun.

She boldly approached. "Sir," she said. "I've read

everything you've written and just want to look at you." She touched the bulky manuscript under her arm. "You see, I am a writer, too."

The humorist looked down at her with a kindly eye, resting his hand on her head. "Of course you are a writer, and don't let anyone discourage you. You will be famous one day."

Whenever she doubted herself she remembered what the great writer had said that day. Finally, in 1959, after fifty years of reworking it, that manuscript was published and became perhaps her greatest triumph, *Dear and Glorious Physician*, the story of the Apostle Luke.

She must have begun this masterpiece, incredibly, when she was seven or eight. But hadn't Mozart composed great music at six or seven? Who knew where aptitudes such as these came from?

She had no Bible training of any kind at this point. Yet she had been obsessed by Luke ever since she could remember. He was the only Apostle that wasn't Jewish-born. He never saw Christ, having not visited the Holy Land until a year after Christ's crucifixion. Everything in his Gospel was hearsay, revealed through meetings with the other Apostles and, apocryphally, with the Mother Mary. Janet had loved Luke from childhood. She saw Luke's search for Christ as a search for God, and later identified it with her own restless search for purpose.

Even as she looked back on this great literary triumph she was not sure what had impelled her. She had begun the first version at nine and finished at twelve. Not satisfied with it as her wisdom grew, she set out at twenty-two to rewrite this novel. At twenty-six she began a third version, stressing the medical, as visions of Luke as a surgeon came to her in overwhelming profusion. Still, she never felt a rightful resolution until she visited Israel in 1956 and traversed ancient roads and byways that seemed now strangely familiar. She felt not only the overpowering presence of Luke, but of One greater than he. She was so moved that she could not speak nor see, for the

tears that filled her eyes. She sank to her knees and prayed that
God would give her the wisdom to finish the book so that it
would light up every man's pilgrimage to the sight of God.
Even now she did not know how she had toiled so long over
this book. She could only quote from the philosopher Nietz-
sche: "One hears—one does not seek; one does not ask who
gives—I have never had any choice about it."

She did not speak wistfully, but analytically, as if to
clarify the present and perhaps foreshadow the future. I was
struck by her openness; it was almost as if she were my subject
and I her biographer.

"I've never had many friends," she said. "I was always
too much inside myself. I never fit in with the other children.
They didn't even exist for me. I was a horrible scholar, except
for English literature, history, and language. They came
without effort. I never did learn math. To this day I can't add
a simple row of figures; that's why I hire lawyers and accountants. And as for division—we never did get together."

She constantly had her knuckles rapped for daydreaming.
It was her only refuge from an unhappy childhood, from
parents who had no sympathy for this strangely adult child.

"Why am I telling you all this?" she demanded.

"Because I'm a good listener." I smiled, wondering, as I
looked about, at the whereabouts of the zealous Marcus; I was
sure he was ordinarily not very far away.

Amazingly, she divined my thought. "Oh, I sent Marcus
off on some important research project"—I thought I detected
an almost imperceptible wink—"so we could speak without in-
terruption."

She returned my smile.

"Listening is a lost art," she said. "I'm not very good at
it myself."

"Yet you wrote *The Listener*?"

"Yes, for God hears, when nobody else does.

"It's so seldom," she went on, "that I find anybody who
won't laugh at me. Mark Twain, Thoreau, Emerson,
Hawthorne, Shakespeare, Keats, all believed there was more to

life than what we taste, touch, or see, but in Buffalo they'd send me off to the booby-hatch if I said so publicly. They consider me a Buffalo housewife who types for a living, though they're not quite sure what it is I type."

She spared no detail in this account, even to her abject horror of poverty from earliest childhood. "We were never without food, and there was always a roof over our heads and a comfortable bed to crawl into. But we had to pinch pennies."

Her father had not been terribly successful, and there was always talk of money, or lack of it. "I remember that when I was about three years old in England I begged my mother to reassure me that we were 'rich,' and not poor like some of the people I encountered on the way to my school. Mama, always anxious to put a kid down—notably me—told me we were not 'rich,' and I was devastated and went out to brood in the. garden, filled with both fear and resolution. I sat down on a boulder near a little fish pond and vowed then—at three—that I would be 'rich' some day.

"At eight, after Mass, in Buffalo, I remained behind to argue with God on the subject. I made a pact with Him. If He would make me 'rich' some day I would give Him one-third of my income 'for the poor.' From the ages of three and eight I never deviated from my determination to have all the money I wanted some day, and I directed my whole life, from earliest childhood, to acquire an education, work hard, and never deviate from my goal, and to 'make it.'"

This determination was not inherited.

"My parents lacked the drive I had and were somewhat timid souls, whereas I was never afraid of anything in the world except the dentist. If my parents had resolute genes, would I not have inherited them? But they did not. I did have my Irish grandmother, whom no one or nothing could get down, but the rest of the family were quiet and retiring with no outstanding talent or ambition. And where did Grandmother get her power of character?"

It was obviously an old story with her, but all new to me

and helpful in understanding her, though I didn't know why
this should matter to me. But I listened closely, every now and
then putting in a question. With her unbroken string of best-
sellers, it seemed to me she must be a walking bank.

"Spending your money must be a problem," I said.

She stared at me, than said matter-of-factly:

"Anonymously, I have helped thousands. I have made
one provision, however: No one is to be helped in any way
with my money unless they have demonstrated guts, drive, ambition, and intelligence. It is a waste of money and effort to
help those who show no desire to help themselves, and no self-
respect.

"I was barely fifteen when I went to work in a factory ten
hours a day. I made the munificent sum of twelve dollars a
week. I had to work at various odd jobs, for I hadn't gone
beyond the eighth grade. And so after a good day in the mill, I
went to night school and learned to be a stenographer and
court reporter, to the day I could use it in my writing."

She rose at six and didn't get home until ten at night, having but one meal and walking to and from home to save
money, for the day when she could find time for writing. After
much perseverance, she convinced her family she could be a
writer, and one Christmas, when she was sixteen, they gave her
an ancient typewriter.

Against this sobering backdrop my eyes fell on the pan-
oply of jewels sparkling warmly in the reflection of the
overhead lights. She caught my look and smiled.

"Do you think," she said, "that my hatred of poverty is
something remembered genetically from another past, like an
animal remembers, or just a child's wish to have the pretty
things she fantasized?"

An errant thought suddenly struck me. Most people had
jobs, but this was not who or what they were; only what they
did. Taylor Caldwell was uniquely what she did. And money
had little to do with it. She would have continued to write if
nobody had published her. She had always written, from the
time she learned to spell when she was four. At her Anglo-

Catholic school in the Manchester suburb of Reddish, she startled her teachers at six by winning a national literary award for an essay on Charles Dickens. After moving to Buffalo she wrote plays and sketches and poems for her Sunday School class. And then her longer things.

Her writing was incomprehensible to her elders. There had never been a writer in the family.

"My father sent my *Atlantis* to my grandfather in Philadelphia, who was with a publishing house. He was horrified. He wrote back that it was impossible for a child to have written so sophisticated a manuscript and said I must have copied it. He urged my father to destroy it. This was the year 1913, and the atom bomb was not even dreamed about then. But I described a nuclear bomb and the havoc it wrought. To this day I don't know where it came from."

Janet gave me a smile, showing her large white teeth. She showed none of the usual aging processes. And for this reason, perhaps, she seemed to delight in talking about aging.

"At twelve, a doctor who examined me for rheumatic fever thought I was twenty-eight or thirty, and I had to show my birth certifcate. When I had my first child I was only eighteen, but the doctor advised me that it was not wise to have children at my age. He thought I was at least forty-two. I married Marcus when I was thirty and he was a generation older, but many people thought I was his age, or was his sister, and once even his mother. It must have been my manner, because I had no wrinkles or gray hair at thirty."

As a child she was known as an "old soul."

"I've been old too long to mind growing old. It's my permanent condition. But, really, I don't believe in old age. My great-grandfather William Muirhead Taylor lived to be one hundred and eight. Each day he would inspect his sheep in the mountains of Ireland, climbing vigorously. Finally, he slipped on ice and fell down a hill, breaking every bone in his body. Still, he lived without medical attention for over a week after that. My grandmother, his daughter, showed me pictures of him. At one hundred he looked like a modern man of fifty. He had a tremendous library and spent hours every day reading, and he never wore glasses. His mind, as well as his body, was eternally young, for he kept them both active and never considered himself old. In fact, he begot his last child, my grandmother, when he was eighty-five and his wife was seventy-two."

I had no idea why she was telling me all this, but I was heartily enjoying myself, for listening to Janet was like reading a Taylor Caldwell novel.

Suddenly she stopped in the middle of a sentence and considered me reflectively.

"I know you better than you think, your past and your future as well. I am quite psychic, you know, and I shall tell you something that will surprise you. You are to write many novels and screenplays, though you think of yourself as merely a reporter. Moreover, you and I shall do several books together. I can't tell you their nature at this time, but they will just naturally develop."

She paused dramatically.

"What is more, in time, your fame will one day exceed my own."

I smiled politely.

"You don't believe it," she said, "but it will happen, and not because my star is fading, for there is much more for me to do before I shuffle off this planet."

She closed her eyes, musing for a moment, then discussed her gift:

"My Irish grandmother used to tell my mother that I was fey, able to see and converse with fairies and have intuitions about the future. Quite often I would say, 'The telephone is going to ring in a minute, and so-and-so will be calling.' It amazed me that people would stare at me in amusement, and I was even more amazed when the phone did ring and their eyes bulged with astonishment."

As a child she heard inner voices and repeated what they said, most of it foreboding. Her family tried to discourage this unpleasant habit because invariably she was the voice of doom, foreseeing death and disaster.

For years she had been making predictions which were invariably correct. "I have deep intuitions about people and events, but every novelist is intuitive, or else what would he write about? I re-read books of mine and wonder at the knowledge that I never knew I had. Where did it originate? Perhaps genetic and racial memory, but what are they? Giving something a name does not explain it.

"I 'remember' one time when I was in my early twenties, during the last of the nineteenth century and possibly into the twentieth. I recall the cool, wide, long street I was walking on, with the houses darkish red stone and large, set back on lawns, and the cool sunshine in which I shivered in my light, cheap skirt and my thin shirtwaist. I wore a cheap straw hat, and I had the red hair I have still. I recall my hopelessness and misery. While I walked down the street I was recalling the mean roominghouse in which I lived and my revulsion at it, and my whole young life I was wishing for death. I knew I was single and I was probably a seamstress or milliner. Nothing more than that. And I am pretty sure it was England. And the name I had was Millie, or Willie, or something like that. And the memory is becoming more and more painful, and I don't know why. Perhaps I committed suicide or something."

She suddenly looked up and studied me gravely.

"Why," she said, "should I remember, when other people don't? You mentioned that sort of thing in your book in speaking of reincarnation."

"Some do," I said, "or we wouldn't have people playing the piano or writing serious music at the age of three of four."

"Then why doesn't everybody remember?"

"I assume it would be too painful for most people."

"It is that, all right," she said. "I've said many times that remembrance ends in the grave, but that doesn't account for the sharp recollections more vivid and real than anything I have experienced on this earth. And it is not all related to this planet. I 'remember' clearly and vividly recalling another planet, a huge, glowing, beautiful planet with no variations of climate, only summer, with three moons. It was so detailed and so personal, so much my home, that why I landed on this little meager earth is something I can't explain. I remember the beautiful Grecian-style house I lived in on that planet, and my husband and my two children, and the intense discontent and dissatisfaction and malaise of the spirit I felt almost always. For I wasn't convinced my husband loved me. Incidentally, there was no 'death' on that planet, but only visible transfiguration, in which the happy person moved on. But where? My 'husband,' though not I, for an inexplicable reason, had the power of transfiguration at will, and it was an awesome sight to see.''

I could hardly visualize short, squat Marcus flitting angel-like through the heavens.

"Are you saying that Marcus changed form and flew from one planet to the other?''

Her eyebrows tilted sharply upward. "I was not speaking of Marcus. He has always been an ordinary man.''

At this moment, Marcus, as if a reincarnation of himself, burst full-blown into the room. He had apparently been hard at work and was in no mood for pleasantries. His lips were clamped together, his eyes stony behind their glasses, and he was altogether gray and grim.

"Janet,'' was all he said, with barely a glance for me.

"All right, my dear,'' she said with a sigh. "I guess it's time for the rat race.''

They were on their way shopping, then back home to Buffalo. "I'll drop you a note,'' she said apologetically. "I have a lot more to tell you. And if you see Lee Barker before I do, tell him that you and I must do a book together.''

Chapter Three

GETTING TO KNOW HER

"I haven't the slightest idea what she wants," said Lee Barker, over the dinner table that evening. "She always means something, but I don't necessarily know what it is. She's completely unpredictable."

My interest went beyond curiosity. I had a feeling of having known her, and yet I had never even read one of her books. She was many years older, yet we had gravitated naturally to a level of equality, free of any inhibition about saying or doing anything that might offend. I had an inexplicable desire to know more about her, as if in searching for whatever it was that brought us together I was really searching for myself.

Why did both of us respond to each other and yet were so unresponsive to others? True, we both grew up in upstate New York and had a common folkway, but others similarly situated had no similar reactions. Mystic Edgar Cayce had attributed instant love or hate to subconscious recognition of the past. But how could one consider anything like this without some shred of evidence?

"Tell me about her," I said, as the abstemious Barker mulled over his third cup of coffee.

He shook his head. "I wouldn't know where to begin."

"What kind of a person is she?"

His eyes lit up with amusement.

"It all depends what day it is. But I can say it isn't very often she goes overboard on anyone. She is a very private person, with intense likes and dislikes. She relies almost totally on intuition."

No one had greater opportunity to study the various aspects of her life. He not only shared her books, but her personal problems.

"We were lucky to eventually get her after Scribners," he said. "Janet says they didn't like her politics, they being liberal, and she conservative, believing in rugged individualism, minimal government, and all that."

What did politics have to do with publishers?

He smiled. "Differences in outlook can be very abrasive, especially with somebody as opinionated as Janet."

Success had not come till she was forty, when she published *Dynasty of Death*, and so while she relished her new-found wealth, it had not basically affected her thinking.

"They had been poor so long," said Barker, "that they couldn't get used to being rich. Marcus was making $6,000 a year as a customs inspector, and they were living in a small apartment in that dreadful place, Buffalo, when *Dynasty* became a runaway best-seller. It took them a while to buy a house and move into it. They had no idea when the bubble might burst. Until she made it, Marcus thought of her as a scribbler. He even destroyed some of her early manuscripts in his vexation at playing second fiddle to a typewriter."

She had married Marcus in the depths of the Depression, in 1931. Peggy, the only child of her first marriage to William Combs, was eleven then, and they were living in a flat over Coogan's drugstore. They came up a bit, with both of them working, moving into a two-family frame house. Peggy had been in convent school, but was pulled out. She had little schooling after that, as Janet kept her at home and tutored her. An uneasy truce existed between Marcus and his stepdaughter until she married a successful young businessman, Jerry Fried, in 1940, and moved out. Marcus and Peggy were never friends, not since the day of the wedding, when she called him "Father," and he turned on her, glowering, and said, "Never call me that again. I am always Mister Reback to you."

Janet dismissed it as one of Marcus's idiosyncrasies, rather than give up on the marriage before it started.

In 1936, the Immigration Department transferred Marcus to New York City. They lived there two years, Janet working furiously on *Dynasty* while haunting publishers' offices. She would show snatches of her manuscript to anybody who would look at it. "Wait till you're finished," she was told. She was encouraged by Lois Cole, a senior editor at Macmillan, one of the few to recognize the Caldwell flair before the public discovered her. She was outvoted by her colleagues. But Janet remembered, dedicating a book to this editor, though Macmillan never published her.

She had a profound respect for Barker. He had a sure touch for best-sellers, even before he became an editor. As a salesman for Houghton Mifflin, he had pushed *The Robe* by Lloyd Douglas, after even the booksellers had given up on it, and then watched it become one of the biggest best-sellers ever. He had schooled Arthur Hailey into his best-sellers *Hotel* and *Airport*, influenced Herman Wouk, and had been Somerset Maugham's American editor. He was Janet's editor for many years now, and a trusted friend and adviser. He had been to Buffalo many times and was considered "family."

He was a saturnine man, a little cynical, a little whimsical, but with all the disappointments and frustrations in being an editor, he had never lost his liking for writers. And Janet, particularly. Whatever she was, she was never boring. An aristocrat himself, a Boston Brahmin from a Pilgrim family, he liked the fact that success had never turned her head.

"For the most part," he said, "she has simple tastes. Her house is solid and comfortable, but not ostentatious. She keeps a housekeeper, who does the cooking, and a maid comes to clean up. There is no sprawling estate, which she could well afford, no host of servants, no fleet of automobiles. She loves to travel, and she and Marcus go all over the globe, ostensibly researching her books. But her research seldom jibes with other people's research, so I think she makes most of it up."

As fanciful as she was, there was a practical side.

"Marcus handles her contract arrangements, but she approves everything," he said. "She's an astute businesswoman, perhaps overly cautious. She puts a ceiling on royalty payments each year, stretching out the payments for tax purposes and for the sense of security it gives her. If she never wrote another line her accumulating royalties would easily go on for another fifty or sixty years, until 2025, in fact. And since she's sixty now, there isn't much chance she will be around to collect.

"Yet with all her caution I have never seen anybody with more zest for life. Just mention a party, and she'll fly down to New York on an hour's notice. She loves gaiety and parties, if the food is good, the atmosphere elegant, and the company scintillating.

"Janet is a phenomenon, and she deals in phenomena. She'll do a book like *Dear and Glorious Physician* and talk about all her research. And then you discover that what makes it so fascinating is what she could not possibly have looked up—all of it new, compelling, and sometimes esoteric. There may very well be two Taylor Caldwells, the skilled novelist, coolly distilling fact and imagination, carefully mapping out a plot with drama and suspense, and the mystic through whom a constant stream of images flows unbidden.

"Frankly, I was not high on *Dear and Glorious Physician* when it first came up. Janet had never done a Biblical novel before, and with the exception of *Quo Vadis* and *The Robe*, novels of Christ usually had little vogue."

Janet's protagonist, St. Luke, had been cut in a heroic mold, a rebel against the fatalism of ancient medicine. His treatment of the White Sickness (leukemia), the Sweet Sickness (diabetes), and numerous other disorders, along with the meticulous description of his surgery, were so realistic that doctors marveled that anybody but a physician could have portrayed all its glowing detail with such empathy.

Luke went beyond medicine. God became the adversary, inflicting sickness and the agony of death on the innocent and unwary. Turning his back on an unjust God, the physician solemnly took a vow to overcome this merciless foe in the fight for life. But later, influenced by Christ's spirit, he turned back to God and began healing the sick by His presence. He never saw Christ, but envisioned him through His mother's eyes. Historically, there was no basis for the meeting with Mary, or for Luke's psychic healings, but these pages, Barker felt, rang with a truth that made the book.

Some of it ran on, appearing repetitious to an editor concerned with a book's pace.

"From a publisher's standpoint, with the cost of paper and printing what it is, there was almost too much detail, and this was true of many of her books. But she would never permit any of this to be trimmed. I got the idea that she didn't want her descriptions of people and places changed because she had experienced them herself, as outlandish as that seems."

I had no idea how Barker personally stood on the occult. Professionally, he was a pioneer in this field, having edited and published Maury Bernstein's trail-blazing *Search for Bridey Murphy*, which stirred a national controversy in claiming a previous lifetime in Ireland for an ordinary Colorado housewife, but was later attacked as a hoax, by a magazine which had been denied publication rights.

Like myself at this time, he felt reincarnation too pat an answer to the mystery of a universe which seemed pointless without some continuity. "It is almost too plausible," he observed.

At this point I really didn't know what she believed, except for the upcoming holocaust. I had once picked up *Dynasty of Death*, but discouraged by its massiveness, had put it down after leafing through its myriad pages.

Barker laughed sympathetically. "Janet calls them her whoppers. You must read her. Like Maugham she's constantly writing about herself. I think she sees herself as the heroine of every seduction scene and the model of every struggling young person who seeks his fortune against insuperable odds."

I didn't find this odd. "But aren't many first novels autobiographical?"

"Oh, yes," Barker replied, "but when somebody has done twenty novels or more, you'd think they'd run out of experiences.

"There is a recurring theme in her novels. The heroes or heroines, driven by passion and ambition, scrabble and scratch their way to the top and find no happiness. Infidelity and sensuality are rampant; duplicity, greed, betrayal commonplace. In *A Prologue to Love*, two brothers love the same woman, who is married to one of them. She, of course, doesn't love her husband. Chicanery is the rule. There is usually one honest person, and he comes off as a victimized simpleton."

He looked up with a smile.

"Can you imagine who?"

I shook my head.

"Janet, of course. That's how she sees herself, in one aspect. But she is also the grand dame who looks down at all this antlike striving from the Olympian heights of a jaundiced wisdom."

Other writers took similar postures. So what made her different, set her apart from the Hemingways and the Steinbecks and the Pearl Bucks, who had more currency with the critics, but despite their vogue couldn't claim the same loyalty among readers.

"You have a feeling she's been there," said Barker. "You can almost taste and smell the situations and places. And since art and life aren't quite the same, her books overflow with the conglomerate spontaneity of real people who don't submit to the disciplines of art. The critics groan, obsessed with literary style and stringent prose, but the readers, artlessly unprejudiced, are lost in the world of romance and intrigue more alluring and realistic than their backyards."

He thought a moment, searching for an example of this extraordinary impact. "In one of her early books, *The Arm and the Darkness*, for instance, she describes the old Paris so well that Parisian journalists marveled at her description."

"Any clear-eyed reporter or novelist might have done as well," I said, thinking of Dumas and Victor Hugo.

Barker's smile broadened. "But Janet had never been to Paris."

She had two projects going with Doubleday, *A Pillar of Iron*, about the Rome of Cicero, and a mystery thriller, *The Late Clara Beame*.

The Late Clara Beame—and Cicero?

Barker smiled. "Janet feels a curious rapport with the people of the Biblical period and with a Rome which parallels the early Christian era."

"So she's imaginative; she's writing an historical novel. Novels don't pretend to be factual. What has that to do with *The Late Clara Beame*?"

"She is a mystery fan. She finishes an Agatha Christie or a Dashiell Hammett or a John MacDonald in an hour or two. 'There is nothing to them,' she keeps saying, 'a child could put them together.' Actually, it's a specialized form. The characters should be well-developed, there has to be suspense, some feeling about the murder victim, and enough plot so the reader doesn't feel cheated."

Janet had pooh-poohed all this, so he dared her to write a whodunit, and she took the dare. She was having unexpected problems.

How could anybody write a novel as obviously complex as *Dynasty of Death* and have any problem with a simple little mystery?

He chuckled. "It's not a flow-through. She is convinced helpful spirits come to her when the rest of the world is sleeping. Apparently, they don't like mysteries."

There was little written about her outside of literary reviews, which I dredged out of the newspaper files. They were generally grudging, even when acknowledging her distinction, patently offhand in the way they dismissed her as a story-teller. She was not classed with the top rank of her contemporaries, but lumped together indifferently with such confirmed lady story-tellers as Fannie Hurst, Edna Ferber, and Frances Parkinson Keyes. One got the impression she would not have been reviewed at all had it not been for her popularity.

Whatever her sources, she was certainly prolific, doing at least one book a year. Beginning with *Dynasty of Death* in 1938, she had published *The Eagles Gather* (1940); *The Earth Is the Lord's* (1941); *The Strong City* (1942); *The Arm and the Darkness* (1943); *The Turnbulls* (1943); *The Final Hour* (1944); *The Wide House* (1945); *This Side of Innocence* (1946); *There Was a Time* (1947); *Melissa* (1948); *Let Love Come Last* (1949); *The Balance Wheel* (1951); *The Devil's Advocate* (1952); *Never Victorious, Never Defeated* (1954); *Tender Victory* (1956); *The Sound of Thunder* (1957); *Dear and Glorious Physician* (1959); *The Listener* (1960); and *A Prologue to Love* (1961).

After her third hit, *The Earth Is the Lord's*, a wonderfully realistic romance about the young Genghis Khan, she decided to put out a book under a nom de plume, to find out how much her new celebrity had to do with her continued success. Her publisher joined in the little game, and *Time No Longer* was published that same year, 1941. The author was "Max Reiner." The unknown didn't have a chance against the smashing success of the young Manslayer from the frozen tundra of Tibet and was never heard from again.

I had read several of her books by now and thought I knew quite a bit about her. But I was still surprised weeks after our first meetings, to find that she was still looking to me for assistance. She had taken some time to write, her letter consisting of several single-spaced typewritten pages. She was still concerned with her metaphysical experiences, relating them in great detail and seeking my reaction.

"I hope," she wrote, "that you can throw some light on these experiences and assure me that I am not completely off my rocker. I have a feeling you know what I am getting at. Otherwise, you could not have written about the metaphysical and psychic the way you did in *The Door to the Future*.

"Before we came to America, I was visiting a large country house in England with my parents. Our hosts were friends of my father and mother, and they had several children. I remember one very clearly, a girl named Alice, about fourteen. She showed me a book she had been reading, *The Mill on the Floss*, and I took it in my hands and said, 'This is my favorite book over all the others I had written.' The kids looked at me with their mouths open, and I heard myself telling them about the story—though, of course, at six I had not read it and had never heard of it before. Then I came to myself with a shivering jolt and put the book down. I've never forgotten that. When, years later, I did read the book, I knew every word of it and where the author had had some trouble and where she had been 'stuck.'

"Now, surely, no one is going to tell me that once I was Mary Ann Evans, known as George Eliot! I couldn't bear it. It would prove reincarnation. It is very odd, though. Long before I read *The Mill on the Floss*, or any other of Eliot's books, I had already won, in my Buffalo school, some prizes for essays and short stories. I was about thirteen then. My teacher told me, 'You know, Janet, you write just like George Eliot!' It was then that I bought *The Mill on the Floss*."

In much the same way, she was familiar with the Victorian poet Algernon Swinburne and could recite endlessly from his verse, not having read any of it.

"My favorite poem," she wrote, "is Swinburne's 'Garden of Proserpine.'

I am tired of hope and laughter
Of men who sow to reap,
Of what may come hereafter,
Of men who live and weep.
I am weary of days and hours,
Blown buds of barren flowers,
Desires and dreams and powers,
And everything but sleep.

"When I was a child of seven, I had not heard of Swinburne, yet I had a 'dream' of a bearded man's study, in the gloomy and heavy English fashion, and a man stood there and he was quoting a poem to me, and then he said, 'I will write that poem, and it will be called *The Lost Garden*.' He then repeated a stanza, and I woke up. But I remembered the stanza. Years later, I discovered Swinburne and found he had, indeed, written *The Lost Garden*—but that stanza was not in it—though it was of the same meter!

Where the northernmost tip of the westerly mountain
Hangs falcon-like over the heart of the bay,
Past seven sad leagues and a last lonely fountain,
A mile from tomorrow the dead garden lay.

"Not the 'lost' garden, you will notice. 'The dead garden.' And that stanza has haunted me all my life—from the time I was seven, when I did not know what a 'league' was, or a 'falcon,' either.

"Do you know the poem which gives me the greatest courage of all, and firms my resolution when I feel most overcome with grief, and comforts me? Yeats:

Draw rein, draw breath,
Cast a cold eye, on life,
On death.
Horseman! Ride by.

She had toyed with the idea of reincarnation, as had Emerson, Thoreau, Mark Twain, and others, but saw no proof of it. And yet she was interested, or she would not be seeking an explanation of her remarkable visual recollections which offered more, spiritually and romantically, than genetic memory or Jung's idea of the atavistic collective unconscious.

She had pondered the intricacies of this Eastern concept, which most of the world believed in except for the pragmatic West. She had considered its various ingredients. Karma, the law of retribution, carried over from one life to the next; *deja vu*, the feeling of having known strange people or places before, the different changes that presumably took place in sex, race, and position. She had read that certain astrological aspects reflected a person's reincarnation pattern, noting with interest the triplicity of earth signs formed by the three of us who had now come together: Barker, a Capricorn; she, a

Virgo; and myself, a Taurus.

"That may be why we all get along so handsomely," she said.

Should there be reincarnation, which she could hardly credit even while toying with the idea, she balked at coming back as anything but a woman. She liked being a woman, and a British woman at that, though she cherished the Roman as the first woman of antiquity to achieve a place of dignity in the home. "I am very fond of men, and I like my role as a woman, with all the superior advantages that women have, thanks to our men who are still chivalrous in spite of Women's Lib. No woman has ever been an authentic genius of the stature of man, but that does not bother me. It is our nature, and I am content with it.

"One life suffices me. It is all I want, or ever hope for, for life, even for the most fortunate, is not truly happy. As Voltaire said:

This world, this theatre of pride and wrong,
Swarms with sick fools who prate of happiness.

"I see no proof of reincarnation. I have thought I have seen spirits or ghosts on occasions, and that they spoke to me. But it's probably a delusion. So much of life is.

"One of the things that amuses me about many who believe in reincarnation is that they are firmly convinced they were Cleopatra, or Queen Elizabeth, or Mary, Queen of Scots, Queen Victoria, a President, a King, a prince, a philosopher, a famous poet, or great and notorious beauties or geniuses. Thousands make the same vehement claims to be somebody. None were quiet housewives or humble breadwinners. It is human nature, I suppose, to rebel at ordinariness, and if the one life is drab, people daydream of bygone or future splendors.

"Obscurity can be a fire of ambition to those who have stalwart souls and a loathing for poverty and anonymity. The stalwart soul has the will and is eager for the race, but the feeble soul merely whines and claims that the ubiquitous 'they' oppressed him and prevented him from attaining what it calls 'my potential.' Fundamentally, character is destiny, and character lies in the genes.

"As Goethe said:

So must thou be.
Thou canst not self escape,
So erst the Sybils, so the Prophet told,
Nor time nor any power can mar the shape
Impressed, that living must itself unfold.

"Some may take this as a belief in karma, but that's pushing it a little.

"There is one thing—among others—which puzzles me. One of my grandsons—I have been a grandmother since I was thirty-nine—used to insist when he was only three or four that he had been born and had lived in India, and babbled about his wife and children there and all about Bombay, and he would beg his parents to take him to India to 'find' 'his people.' He is blond and blue-eyed and certainly does not resemble an Indian. Moreover, his knowledge of Buddhism was amazing. I have no explanation of it. I do know that now in his middle twenties he lives very austerely and will not touch beef, and that he has a reverence for all life, which we in the Western world do not. He has not told me—I am a Westerner of Westerners—but I 'feel' that he has a profound aversion for Western standards and is enamored of the East. There is an intense lack of sympathy between us, which I carefully respect, and I have seen in his blue eyes a shadow I cannot comprehend. Often he looks hopelessly desperate, but are we not all desperate one way or another?"

Chapter Four

RAGS TO RICHES

"Why," I asked, "does she wear so damn many jewels?"

"Janet always likes to be the center of attention."

I was living in New York at this time, and I usually saw Lee Barker at least once a week, and I had never been with him that I didn't learn something that influenced my work. Our friendship went beyond work, leading to an atmosphere of trust in which I felt free to explore any subject, knowing I would receive a straightforward answer.

I could see he was amused by my doubting look.

"It certainly caught your attention," he said. "Actually, there's never a simple explanation with Janet. She has impulses that she doesn't quite understand herself, though she may develop some theory about it. She studies herself like she does the characters in her novels, and then becomes one."

"The jewels are inconsistent," I said, "for I have the feeling there is nothing ostentatious about her."

"Oh, she likes a certain amount of glitter. I suppose it's compensation for the drabness of her early life. She grew up in poverty and, to hear her tell it, was supporting herself when she was nine or ten. All that jewelry in a way is her badge of success." He laughed suddenly. "Even if she does carry her jewels around in a brown paper bag like a ham-and-cheese sandwich."

I had an idea that Janet stretched things a little.

"Was she really working at that age?"

"Oh, yes, running errands, mowing lawns, scrubbing the neighbors' floors, baby-sitting—anything to bring money and make her independent. She had the work habit almost from the cradle."

I had already learned much about her from the books of hers I had read. She was a conservative, politically, believing the spoils belonged to those who toiled for them. There were no free lunches. She abhorred the welfare philosophy that gave handouts to free-loaders, decrying rewards for indolence and incompetence. This shrill tone ran through her books to a point where it was almost a litany, whether the stage was Tibet, China, France, Rome, New England, or some distant planet of her imagination.

"You must understand," Barker said, "that Janet is an agin-er. It's the Irish in her. She loves a good scrap and will say things just to be outrageous, taking either side with equal fervor."

Her quick intuition intrigued me. And one thing mystified me beyond others. I was still amazed that she should have picked out passages in my then unpublished book. "How did she ever do that?" I asked, "when it wasn't even published?"

Barker smiled. "I don't like shattering your illusions, but I sent her the galley proofs."

"Had you ever sent her any other galley proofs?"

"Not that I remember."

It was a productive lunch, and though doing another book of my own, I had decided to give priorities to my budding library of Caldwell blockbusters.

"And how," I asked, "is the lady progressing on *Cicero* and *Clara Beame*?"

"*Cicero* is doing fine, constantly expanding. Did you know that he and his arch-enemy, Catiline, loved the same girl?"

I had read much about the Catiline conspiracy, but this

morsel had somehow escaped me.

"I don't know where she digs these things up," Barker continued, "but they certainly add spice to an old story."

"And *Clara Beame*?"

He shook his head. "There are two Taylor Caldwells, as I said. One stands back like a pitcher and lets fly, the other tries to find the plate—and misses." He sighed. "It's not the breather we thought."

There was a glint of amusement on that sardonic countenance.

"I told her she should dream about Clara Beame. But she got annoyed."

With *Clara Beame* I thought she was dropping below the margin of her talent.

"Don't you find her something of a genius?"

"What makes you say that?"

"She has an unfathomable way of producing the unique, beyond the usual logic and reason."

"No writer is a genius to his editor, but she's certainly an enigma."

Nevertheless, she did share the attributes of genius. Einstein had admittedly come upon his relativity theory mystically; Edison had visualized the light bulb and the phonograph in daydreams. Elias Howe saw his sewing machine in his sleep; Robert Louis Stevenson dreamed his most imaginative stories. And Taylor Caldwell seemed to invoke exciting fragments of the past by merely closing her eyes or staring off into space.

If she had any craft, I couldn't detect it.

"Has she developed any techniques over the years?" I asked.

"Not really. *Dynasty of Death*, her first book, could very well be her best. Janet talks a lot about her research, but as I said, I don't see any sign of it. She makes it up, but somehow it doesn't seem made up."

Yet she listed extensive bibliographies and boasted of her research, and Marcus's.

His shrug was eloquent.

"That may be, but she seldom allows a fact to interfere with her fancies."

In some books she was more self-involved than others. *Never Victorious, Never Defeated*, written for another publisher, he considered Janet's favorite looking-glass.

"You don't give up, never, but you don't win, ever, since fate has a nasty way of plucking the prize just when it is about to fall in your grasp."

Like her others, this book was massive. I thumbed through it with dismay, but after the first few pages I was hooked. This novel about railroads and banking had come out ten years before, in 1954, when Janet was fifty-four. Again I marveled at the intimate insight into things she ordinarily wouldn't have known about. There was the usual intrigue and chicanery, pure soap opera in its continuing vicissitudes, if not for the force that made her characters leap out of the pages. There were many faces of Taylor Caldwell in her heroine, the cool, calculating, piratical, yet charming, Cornelia. Cornelia was at nineteen a juicy plum, hotly sought after by every man with an eye for beauty. She had a bold eye, long lissom limbs, a willowy body, and her gleaming gowns, beaded with diamonds, were designed to reveal her own glittering charms. Obviously, this was Taylor's dream, for at age nineteen she was dirt poor, prospecting with her first husband in the bleak West Virginia hills, and dressed in rags. It was the way she saw herself, adding only the finery.

Cornelia wore well. At an age when Janet was savoring her first literary triumph, she saw Cornelia at thirty-nine tempered by events into a finer, more enduring metal: "Her face was tighter, more strongly chiseled than in youth, harder and more astute, cubical lines about a mouth which depended these last few years on paint rather than on young blood for its color, her cheeks rouged expertly, but lacking their original roundness and the flare of natural tint. However, nothing could extinguish the power, the light, the indomitable passion of her character fully revealed in her eyes. Nothing but death would ever quiet or subdue them, or drain from them their bawdy gleam and strength.''

This, I imagined, was how she really was. She might bend, but not break; she grew older, but not old. Aging, with its deteriorating process, was not for Cornelia—nor Janet Taylor Caldwell. Nineteen passed, thirty-nine, the fifties, and then, prophetically, the Biblical three score and ten—seeing herself at seventy:

"When she stood she was five feet eight inches tall, and her figure might have been that of a woman forty years her junior. Her waist was slim, her breast full and white, though the neck above it was raddled. She could stride like a young woman, and her gestures were quick and dominant. She could ride a horse like a young man, and she often drove her own car. She could swim like a vigorous child, swear like a New York policeman, outshout anyone at a football game, and dance like an adolescent. She also had an original and very large fund of ribald stories and could outdrink almost any man. She smoked constantly.''

I read on with a smile, mindful of our first meeting, when I saw her down an impressive quantity of bourbon, commenting as she smacked her lips that it was a satisfying 100 proof. As I recalled, she had not picked at her food that night, but applied herself with gusto to a well-prepared meal. And now again she was dining in all the glitter she fancied.

"A diamond necklace blazed about her throat, diamonds glittered in her ears, in her hair and on her fingers, and all up and down both long white arms. It was a crude display. But then Cornelia had never pretended to have taste. She was vulgar and raucous and coarse, and gloried in it all. She displayed her vulgarity as she displayed her diamonds: proudly, and with wicked humor.''

Perhaps Barker was right. Who knew better than she why she made her dazzling displays of diamonds and rubies? Who knew better the rebellious nature that liked to shock the smug and the rich, to parody their wealth and position while herself enjoying as much. She was not of them, for she had the gift of laughing at herself while mocking the society that accepted her for her gifts. She was the central figure of a massive charade, and her surface politeness, finery, and jewels cloaked a ribald earthiness that was the terror of well-bred hostesses. Of course this explained my urgently extended invitation by Neltje Doubleday—as a buffer against any outburst of embarrassing irreverence.

While acknowledging some inroads of time, she still conceded little to age, again prophetically.

"Above this amazing face was an even more amazing pile of waves and shining red hair interwoven with diamonds. It was not auburn red, or a sandy red, or a golden red. It was frankly and simply, violently red. It was the color of her youth. She had portraits to prove it. For the past thirty years, however, her hair had been really white. She did not care who knew that this redness she now displayed was only a dye. It was a work of art, and it was abundant and vigorous."

And so with success came the stilted world of society. Yet never far from the surface was the loneliness and misery of childhood. She seemed riveted to this period, unable to break out of the aridness of being unloved and alone, having nowhere to turn, not even to God, for He was someone they scared you with in church, a threat when all else failed. In all this forlornness she was clearly the child in *A Prologue to Love.*

"The gusts of wind lifted the child's braids and blew wisps over her poor coat. But the child did not move; she huddled on her stone. It was as if she were waiting mournfully yet eager, as a woman waits for the return of her love who has been long gone from her sight. She was unaware of her cold hands, which were reddened and without gloves, and of her cold feet in shabby buttoned boots, and her icy knees covered meagerly with darned black stockings."

There was, as Barker said, some part of Janet, mingled with fancy, in every book she wrote. In *Prologue* she was no cynical Cornelia, but the hypersensitive, motherless Caroline, unloved, thinking herself unattractive, friendless.

Caroline's father detested her, and when he spoke to her

at all, it was about avoiding poverty, a condition which had dogged Janet through her early life and led her to observe once: "Cold cash is a girl's best friend."

From her father Caroline learned poverty had no virtues: "Fools say that poverty is no crime, but it is. The world impresses that on you very severely. It treats you much worse when you're poor than if you were a murderer or a madman. And the poor are even more vicious toward the poor than the rich are; they never forgive you for being one of them."

Caroline's father was determined to destroy any illusions that would make his daughter tolerant of poverty.

"Money," he said, "is the only thing that can stand between you and hate and persecution and hunger. People may talk stupidly about family and position and name. These are nothing if you are poor. For when you are poor you have no family and no position and no name."

Caroline, like Janet, came to realize the value of money. "This power did not come from love, from tidy walls, from little gardens and chickens, from warm kitchens, from the voice of any man, no matter how beloved and how needed. It came only from money."

But money and power, as important as they were, paled before that great leveller—death, as revealed in its bare bones in this lament from *This Side of Innocence*:

"The only inevitable thing was man's suffering and man's death. Yet, when these came to him, the average man was stunned and incredulous and despairing. He had no philosophy for the inevitables. They were catastrophes and calamities, the inexplicable, the events that ought not to have occurred. Yet man should know that he would suffer, that he would face death, and lose to death all that was significant and dear to him. To prepare for agony, for parting, ought to be part of the education of every human being."

Fear of death was an ugly thing as she had her character conclude: "But there was hope. Always hope, if not in this world then another.

"He looked at the sky, and suddenly he was full of a calm

ecstasy, a kind of rapturous realization. It was not faith. It was something much deeper, much tenderer, much more profound. It is enough, he thought, and it is enough to compensate for a lifetime of suffering and sadness and struggle that we have had that moment or two of ecstasy which accompanies the knowledge of the being of God, and of the meaning of man, and the peace that comes with the light that 'never was on sea or land.'"

It was doubtful that she had found this peace, for she was still searching, still striving with that keen consciousness to define her own purpose in life and to fathom, in her own way, whether death was the end-all.

"I have memories of the past," she had written me, "but how do I know they are not some forms of racial consciousness, as postulated by Jung, or just errant figments of my imagination."

She was the eternal iconoclast. She saw the smallest chinks in our society, and out of her perception came a feeling of despair at the feeble ineffectuality of man in the relentless march of events. Where could God be hiding when a Hitler could sweep the world like Attila the Hun and reduce the dignity of man to a shambles? She was especially touched. Her native England stood virtually alone, and her husband was piously Jewish.

She found Hitler an almost comic figure, but there was no laughing him off with his hordes sprawled over Europe threatening the civilized world. She went to sleep one night troubled by thoughts of Hitler, and during the night she dreamed of another conqueror, Genghis Khan. She no longer needed to look for parallels. She now had a conqueror so destructive that even Hitler paled before him. Out of this dream came, with a wealth of detail, the Mongol chieftain's saga, prophetically titled *The Earth Is the Lord's*.

Ridicule, she knew, was the sharpest weapon against tyrants. "Any resemblance," she wrote, "between the character of this novel and personages living today is indignantly denied by the author! Ghost of Genghis Khan should notify author if such libelous rumor begins to circulate.''

It was not her nature to keep to the sidelines when things she loved were going down. The times had changed, but the scourge of the barbarian was the same.

Considering the time, 1941, when a gasping Europe lay at Hitler's feet, considering the wide audience of this brilliant new literary star, there was a ring of hope in her foreshadowing the end of the new anti-Christ. She had watched films of Hitler's happy jig after the abject French surrender, and in that moment, intuitively, she had tuned into the dictator's own secret doubts.

"He was suddenly aware of some terrible presence, of some unsleeping Eye, some most ominous regard. For an instant, his heart quailed, and his hand dropped. Then, lifting his eyes, he gazed at the brightening immensity of the skies, and his whole spirit was filled with triumph and defiance, fury and savage joy.

"'I have the world,' he cried, and his voice seemed to sound like a trumpet note in the silence. 'I, Genghis Khan, am the world.'

"Only silence answered him, unbroken and contemptuous and awesome. Only the silence of God replied.

"And the eyes of God saw everything, and the silence of God swallowed up the universe, and the spirit of God seemed to flow out upon the earth, invincible, conquering and ever victorious.''

Chapter Five

OF LOVE AND MARRIAGE

MY *Door to the Future* had finally come out in the spring of 1963. She wired congratulations, and said she would be in New York to launch two books, *Grandmother and the Priests* and *The Late Clara Beame*.

I was surprised that she and Marcus accepted an invitation to drop in at my New York apartment, and decided the success of a recent book, *The Sixth Man*, which had jumped onto the best-seller list, and now of the *Door to the Future*, may have allayed his suspicions of some nobody capitalizing on his wife's career. At any rate, he was quite friendly and amiable, in contrast to our previous meetings—almost jovial, in fact, speaking to me now as if we were kindred spirits with the cold-blooded publishers our common adversary.

I marveled that after some thirty years of marriage they sat together on the davenport holding hands and billing and cooing. It was a side of Janet I had not seen before.

"It's very touching," I said, "you two sitting there like teen-agers."

She gave him an affectionate smile.

"We're just doing that," she said, with a fond glance, "so we don't wallop each other."

She had married Marcus when she was thirty-one having known for years she was going to marry somebody named Marcus R. She knew this even before her first marriage to a young sailor named William Fairfax Combs. She was thirteen, she recalled, when she had her first indication of her future marriages, to Marcus as well as Combs.

"I was drowsing in my classroom, my hand poised over a piece of paper and holding a pen, when my hand began to move by itself."

She had written down two strange names, those of two husbands, in order, as it turned out. It didn't mean anything to her at the time. And then three years later, at sixteen, she saw their faces on a letter she was typing.

A year later, at seventeen, with America's entry into World War I, she enlisted in the Navy as a yeoman first class. Installed in wartime Washington, she fell in love with a young Marine officer about to be shipped overseas. Then, as she was about to marry him, she met a young sailor. His face was familiar, but she couldn't remember why, and then it dawned on her.

"Your name wouldn't be William Fairfax McCombs?" she asked.

The young man drew back in amazement. "Yes, it is," he said, "but we dropped the *Mc* two hundred years ago."

She broke her engagement, marrying Combs two months later. After the war they retired to the mountains of West Virginia and turned to prospecting. They had one child, Mary Margaret, Peggy. The marriage rocked along for a few years, Janet not only handling the domestic chores, but chopping wood, gardening, trapping, even prospecting alongside her husband. For the first time she was unable to find time for her writing. And that was enough in itself to end it.

She returned to Buffalo and was divorced at twenty-four, taking a job as a secretary with a government agency to support her six-year-old child. She had not written a line in six years.

That same year, 1924, she met Marcus. Her office superior, an older man named Kingsley, came in with a short, stocky man of thirty-five with dark features. "I want you to meet a friend of mine," he said.

With a surge of emotion she realized the stranger's name before it was spoken.

She turned to Marcus now, and there were tears of sentiment in her eyes. He looked a little flustered, obviously embarrassed, as if all this sentimentality was alien to his carefully nurtured image of rocklike formidability.

"I looked at him," she said, "with a sudden leap of my heart and tremendous joy and love, and I cried, 'Marcus.'"

Marcus had been alertly following the conversation. His head inclined slightly, as if to confirm that dramatic moment.

He was by nature a dour man, and he scowled as she mentioned his early disapproval of her writing, but brightened now as she gave him a fond smile and said, "Marcus was very involved in *Dynasty*, encouraging me to finish it. He was sure it would be a best-seller. His encouragement kept me going nights when I could hardly keep my eyes open and knew I had to be up early to get on the job myself."

After they moved to New York City, she had struck up a friendship with Lois Cole, the senior Macmillan editor, who recognized she was no ordinary fledgling writer. Cole marveled, as others would later, at the vast wealth of detail about the steel and munitions industries that went into this epic story of a French immigrant family of the early 1800s. In her naïveté, Janet had assumed this interest meant that Macmillan was prepared to publish the finished manuscript. But colleagues, differing from Lois Cole, who saw only the underlying talent, thought the one-thousand page offering clumsy and unwieldy. Cole, disappointed as well, told the dejected Janet she could use her recommendation with any other publisher and suggested the venerable house of Scribners.

The Rebacks had moved back to Buffalo by this time, and they were devastated by this blow.

"I had been writing since a child," Janet recalled, "and nothing had been published. My lifelong dream had become a nightmare. I was ready to give up."

Their Buffalo apartment looked smaller than ever now. Despondent, they wandered aimlessly through the downtown streets one evening. They had no idea where they were going. But their steps took them almost compulsively to the Statler Hotel. Standing outside, in Buffalo's freezing January weather, they read an announcement of a spiritualist meeting inside. The spiritualist, a medium, was the Reverend Doctor Charles Nicholson, from Janet's native England.

"Shall we go in?" Janet whispered.

"Why not?" Marcus shrugged.

They pushed their way through the lobby. Only standing room was available, and hemmed in by the surging crowd they were about to turn away. "Suddenly," recalled Marcus, joining in the conversation, "I saw two people in the front row get up, and I rushed with my wife down the aisle. We were seated just as Dr. Nicholson came to the platform and the demonstration began."

Nicholson spoke quietly of survival and the spirit world, explaining that when the right atmospheric vibration existed there was a radiolike frequency through which the dead could communicate with the living, if not directly, then through a medium. He then shut his eyes, to close off conscious distractions and keep his receiving set clear.

A few messages came through, but nothing significant. It seemed odd to them that the spirits should take the trouble to come all the way from the other side just to ask if so-and-so was in the room, and would he mow the lawn, or see that the flowers were kept up at the grave. It seemed so inconsequential that Janet and Marcus began to fidget restlessly. Nicholson himself appeared bored by the lack of meaningful communication. But, suddenly, as they were about to leave, the spiritualist stood at attention and cocked his head to one side, as if fascinated by what he was hearing. His eyes roamed over his audience, flicking over Janet and Marcus, then traveling to the rear of the room and back to the front row again.

"I have a message from an Arthur," he said finally. "Has anybody here a father named Arthur?"

Janet Taylor Caldwell raised a timorous hand. "My father's name was Arthur," she said.

The spiritualist regarded her with interest, struck, no doubt, by the English accent in this alien area. His voice was cool and crisp, but his eyes floated off as if heeding a direct voice on his open lines of communication.

"Your father," he said, with half an eye on Janet, "tells you not to be discouraged. He knows you have had a bitter disappointment and he sympathizes, but he wants you to know that the manuscript you have written"—Janet and Marcus almost jumped in their seats—"will be published, and it will be successful."

All eyes were now on Janet, and her eyes were on Nicholson. She could barely contain her excitement as the medium continued:

"Your father wants you to know the manuscript will be accepted on April 2 of this year—1938—by another publisher" —and a more dramatic pause—"it will be a great success and establish you as a writer of the first rank."

And this was not all.

"A year from now, after the book has been published, you will be in California discussing a motion picture version of the book."

It seemed an incredible dream, but Janet was considerably buoyed in spirit as she got up from the meeting. Both she and Marcus looked eagerly to the date mentioned by the spiritualist, and meanwhile took the sensible precaution of sending the manuscript off to Scribners.

It went to other publishers, too, with a renewed Marcus directing the operation. There were a few cautious responses. And the Scribners, and their discerning editor Maxwell Perkins, cheerfully agreed to take on the book.

"On April 2," said Marcus, "as the medium had said, we signed a contract with Scribners to publish *Dynasty of Death.* It became the Number One best-seller, and a year later we were in Hollywood discussing the movie."

The overnight success immediately put them into another world. As the royalties poured in from Scribners and publishers abroad, there were new clothes for Peggy and for six-year-old Judy, born a year after this marriage. Taylor said good-bye to the small apartment. Their new house in one of Buffalo's better suburbs bloomed with greenery. At last Janet had breathing room.

"How long," I asked, "was it before you quit your job?"

She snorted. "How long does it take to say goodbye?"

She had a smile for her husband. "Marcus wasn't taking any chances. He stayed on till he got his pension."

Within a year she had tasted the bittersweet trappings of success. Letters of adulation and appreciation for her attack on the munitions makers streamed in. The Nobel Peace Prize committee expressed interest. The leaders of nations, captains and kings, showered her with fan mail. And the money kept pouring in. Janet—and Marcus—had not known there was that much money in the world. It meant also lawyers and accountants, and the Internal Revenue. For weeks on end she hardly found time to write. She was becoming a commodity. And so to get away from it all, she indulged an itch to travel, to see the places and the people storming through her mind's eye in the past.

They traveled to Rome, Paris, London, to the Midlands where she had been born, to Florence, Venice, Milan. And it was all familiar. Always she had the feeling of having been there before, some places more so than others. Some memories took her back inevitably to childhood. Ever since she was three she had had a particularly dreadful dream. In it, she was standing at a small casement window in a tower, looking down with a feeling of anguish on a slanting roof below, covered with dirty red tiles.

There were no such tiled roofs in England, so the dream seemed to have little relevance to her homeland. It was a continuing dream, year after year, and always the same. The sky was cold, dull gray, and the sea of roofs beyond her tower were all jostling red tile too, and seemingly went on for miles. In the distance she saw a river and the stone bridges crossing over. Even at three, she saw herself not as a child but a mature woman, in her twenties, looking about the same, she was to realize later, as she did when she was actually this age. She was a prisoner, a religious of some sort, in nun's habit, put away because she would not recant, would not renounce the fiery priest leading a revolt against corruption in the Church. As terrified as she was, she could not betray him, for he was dear to her.

The feeling of disquietude pervaded her waking hours long after she awakened. She kept hearing footsteps and sat up in her trundle bed expecting to see the three men in the white hoods of Dominican monks, whose scraping footsteps outside her prison had reverberated ominously in her sleep. She had dreamed they were coming to torture her. As she heard a key grating in the lock, she turned to her prison window in despair, knowing this was her only escape. And as the door opened, she threw herself onto the sloping roof, with relief and even joy. And then, as she rolled down the cutting tilt of tiles, she saw only tunnels of darkness. And woke up.

This dream persisted for forty years and more, until her first visit to Italy, with Marcus. They traveled to Rome, then on to Florence, over the protests of Marcus, who saw no reason for the diversion when they still had so much to see in Rome. But Janet felt an irresistible urge to see this great giant of the Renaissance. In Florence, they were the guests of a Count and Countess whose family history was closely inter-woven with that of this once mighty city-state.

She soon knew why she had come to Florence. As the city emerged before her eyes, she saw with a start the tilted red tiles of her dream on nearly every rooftop. Shown to her room in the Count's palace, she looked down from her bedroom win-dow onto a circular plaza, with many streets leading into it like the spokes of a wheel. The plaza was strangely empty, and in the center stood a tall pillar surmounted by a medieval horseman. Suddenly a sensation of utter foreboding swept over her, and she drew the curtains across the window and went to bed, tossing restlessly most of the night.

In the morning she hurried to the window, pulled the draperies, and looked outside.

The plaza was gone. There was a big, broad street outside, and many other streets radiating away from it—but no plaza except for a very small concrete island with a sort of modernistic monument on it. She could not believe her eyes.

She said nothing to her husband and went downstairs to breakfast with the Count and Countess. The Count could not speak a word of English, and she could not speak a word of Italian. The Countess, however, was fluent in English and she acted as interpreter. Casually, Janet mentioned the "plaza" she thought she had seen. The Countess smiled and mentioned it to the Count. He got up and brought a large book to the table and turned several pages, showing her the plaza just as she had seen it earlier. It was an old engraving from the Renaissance period, and there was the prancing horseman high on the pillar, and the gloomy shadowed streets, and the blank sides of buildings. The Count looked at her with a peculiar smile but made no comment.

Later, the Countess took them on a tour of Florence. They came onto another concrete island—and then, before her eyes, the island disappeared and there was another, if smaller, plaza and crowds of people in strange costumes and a whole company of white-robed Dominican monks. In the center of the little plaza a man, also robed in white, was bound to a stake in the bright sunshine, a small plump man with flaming eyes. It was the Dominican prior of San Marco's, who had dared to defy a Pope. Horrified and dazed, Janet cried aloud, "Savonarola!"

The Countess responded unemotionally, "Yes. And that monument is there in his honor," and the scene immediately shifted back to the present reality, and all the people she had seen and the monks disappeared.

Shaken, she went back to the car, telling herself that she must be hallucinating. But there was to be more.

On the way back they stopped to look at the bridges over the river Arno. Her eyes fell on a beautifully carved medieval bridge of white marble with embossed figures on it. She said to the Countess, "Now, there is something really lovely, that bridge.'' As she spoke, the bridge blanked out and there was no bridge in that spot at all. The Countess smiled at her oddly, but made no comment.

They returned to the house. After dinner she was left alone with the Count. Although he did not know English, he spoke now in what seemed perfect English. "I have some very special wine, very old, which I hope you will join me in drinking, for this is an unusual occasion." They drank together and had an animated conversation. She told him of her experiences that day, and he nodded and said, "You have been here before, long ago. I have known of these things all my life." He brought the book he had shown her that morning and opened it to a colored engraving and showed her the bridge she had seen earlier, saying, "It was swept away and lost, at the time of Savonarola."

In a sort of daze, she said, "Count, you speak wonderful, perfect English." He smiled and said, "No. You speak perfect Italian, though in an archaic form." She could not believe it. She called over to the Countess and her husband, who had been conversing in a corner, and said, "Please tell me! Have I been talking to the Count in Italian, and has he been talking to me in English?" Both her husband and the Countess laughed, and Marcus said, "You have been talking in English and he in Italian, but you seemed to understand each other perfectly!" Evidently, they were reading each other's minds, in a language they knew centuries before.

She looked at the Count, and he gave her that mysterious smile again. And then, feeling compelled to confide in him, she told him of the awful dream she had had since she was a child. He listened intently, nodding his head, and then explained, "You lived in Florence at the time of Savonarola, and you must have been one of his followers, and that is why you were condemned to death." He then showed her another engraving of medieval Florence, with the very sort of tall, narrow building in which, in her dream, she had been a prisoner. It was very familiar. And terrifying.

Marcus must have heard the story a hundred times. He

said with a frown, "Now, Janet, there's no point to digging all that up again. People will think you're crazy."

"I thought so myself," she said.

Some purpose appeared to have been served by the incident in Florence. "I never had that dream again," she said. "And I shall never go back to the brooding city in which the Count thought I had lived at one time. I couldn't get away fast enough; we cut our visit short, something my husband did not understand until I told him the story. But the Count understood. He said, 'Now that you were there, there is no more need for the dream to recur.'"

We sat silently for a moment, then shaking myself a little, I asked:

"How long ago did all this happen?"

Marcus had thoroughly researched it, after the act, so to speak.

"Savonarola was martyred in 1498," he said with a voice of authority. "Six years after Columbus discovered America."

Chapter Six

THE MESSIAH

EVEN amid her greatest successes, she was still preoccupied with *our* book.

"What are you doing on it?" she asked.

I still had no idea what was wanted.

"I have discussed it with Barker," I said, "and he has no ideas on it."

She gave a gesture of impatience.

"He wouldn't know, but you should. Think about it, try to remember, and you will know what to do."

She had come down to New York once again to usher in a round of parties marking the launching of *The Pillar of Iron*. It was an immediate success, hitting the 1965 best-seller lists even more swiftly than most of her books. By now, she had built up a huge following, and her name alone᾽ was enough to assure a run on the bookstores. I had gone through the book and found it fascinating. I had read considerably on ancient Rome, somehow feeling a vague kinship with these hard flint-eyed men who had imposed Roman justice on three continents.

As with *Dear and Glorious Physician*, I was struck by her obsession with the mystique of the Messiah. In the one book, he was already gone, a ghost of the past. In this newest venture, he appeared only as a shadow of the future, drawn into the Roman story out of context. In what seemed almost an in-

trusion into the Rome of Cicero and Caesar, a Jewish friend of
Cicero's writes from Jerusalem:

"You ask me again of the Messias [Greek spelling],
though more tentatively than usual. He is still hourly expected!
The Pharisees send priests up and down the length of Israel
searching for the Mother and the Holy Child, while the worldly
Sadducees laugh at them. For the Sadducees call themselves
pragmatic men, and scorn any teachings of the world hereafter
and ridicule the prophesies of the Messias. They prefer
Hellenistic reason. They pause in their gilded litters when a
ragged rabbi, whose feet are dark with dust, speaks of
Bethlehem and the One Who is to be born there of a Maiden
Mother, the Lily of God. But they pause to express mirth and
to shake their heads in wonder at the credulity of the poor and
the homeless who long for their Savior who shall be called
Emmanuel, for He will deliver his people from their sins. But I
no longer smile with the Sadducees. Each night I stand in the
cool brightness of the moon and the stars on the roof of my
house and question Heaven: 'Is He born this hour, and where
shall I find Him?'"

Why was this passage so obviously dragged in? Why was
she so involved in this period? And, more, what was this tie
between us?

She had her daughter Judy with her on this trip. Judy, an
attractive brunette of thirty or so, was clearly her mother's
favorite. Everything denied Janet in growing up was lavished
on her younger daughter. She had cars, furs, private schools,
governesses, coming out parties, and flaming romances that
led to one early marriage and a divorce. She now seemed happily married to a college professor. Marcus was a doting parent
with his own child, but the obvious tandem was mother and
daughter. It was touching to see their adoring glances and their
easy familiarity. Every other word out of Janet was Judy this
or Judy that. They had been shopping on Fifth Avenue, and
everything Janet bought was for Judy. "She is such a delight,"
she said.

We had been sitting around her hotel suite, prior to the

round of dinners, and Barker had been trying to pin her down on her next project.

She frowned, releasing Judy's hand for a moment. "Quite a few things have been stirring in my mind." She gave Barker a quizzical look. "You've probably never heard of Melina; it's a planet in another galaxy, with an interesting history."

He laughed. "How about doing something solid, Saladin and the Crusades, or even Paul, which we talked about. That would be a good follow-up to Luke. Or you might do Mary or Jesus."

She shook her head. "I have been considering a book loosely based on the Kennedy clan. Old Joe Kennedy was a pirate, but a delightful man as well. He came from an immigrant family and rose because of a fierce resolve to lift himself out of the ordinary."

Her interest in the Kennedys stemmed from her own continuing feeling about the President's assassination two years before. At the time, she had sent warnings to the White House, receiving the same polite acknowledgment she would have gotten had she commented on the White House Rose Garden.

Barker appeared interested. "It could be very timely," he said.

"But Melina first," she said, "I'm bursting with ideas."

"And Paul?" he put in. "Your readers expect that."

"Yes," she sighed, "Paul, who was Saul, the inquisitor turned evangelist, the great lion of God. How can I forget?"

We both eyed her curiously, for she spoke as of an old friend.

It was not until later, alone together, that I brought up the Kennedys. Many people had forecast the President's murder, but Janet was the only person I knew to have sent a warning and immersed herself, emotionally, in the life of the family. It was hard to separate the dream from the reality, for she had dreamed his death first and then had flashed onto his father, Ambassador Joseph Kennedy, and caught a glimpse of that domineering, single-minded personality, which she was to translate into a phenomenal success story in *Captains and the Kings*.

"I was not thinking of the President," Janet explained, "when I had this dream in which Marcus and I were watching television. As a program came on, I turned to Marcus and said, 'President Kennedy is going to be murdered.' Marcus shook his head in disbelief. But as we kept watching television, a scene with the President came on in color, though our set is black and white. And Marcus now appeared to see it as well. The President was sitting in an open car; there were people next to him, but I couldn't make them out. Kennedy was dressed in a gray suit and a striped tie, and he was smiling. I heard a loud report, clearly that of a gun, then two or three more shots, and the President half-rose in his seat, then fell back, bleeding from his head."

When she woke that morning, the dream was still so vivid that she was sure the President had been assassinated. She hurried downstairs to the dining-room, where her husband was having breakfast, and cried out:

"The President has been killed!"

She turned on the TV, expecting a news report. But the morning soap operas were on as usual.

I had no wish to ruffle her feathers, but many psychics, and astrologers as well, had forecast the President's death.

"Are you aware," I said, "that every President elected at twenty-year intervals since 1840 has died in office? And the astrologers predicted it because of an astrological cycle which seems to affect the United States Chart."

"That is strange, isn't it?" she said, making some rapid calculations: President Harrison, 1840; Lincoln, 1860; Garfield, 1880; McKinley, 1900; Harding, 1920; Franklin Roosevelt, 1940; and Kennedy in 1960.

What do you see for 1980?" I asked.

"I have no feeling about astrology," she said. "But I do feel we will be in for some momentous changes."

This information flowed into her brains and books from a source outside herself and had nothing to do with her own powers, she insisted. It was something far more mysterious and significant.

"I have never discussed this with anybody, not even my husband, and I am not sure I should now, for it may not be safe for you."

Her voice fell to a whisper, and I had to lean forward to catch the last words.

"I am not concerned," I said.

"You are either a very brave or foolish man. For Darios is not one to be trifled with. Even I hesitate to take his name lightly, for he is like the Archangel Michael, a very stern and inexorable Master, present always when you least expect him."

After she sat down to write in the early hours of the morning, Darios would appear in a burst of light, a brilliant radiance that she could not look at directly. He was nebulous, a presence, the brother of the fallen Lucifer, and in constant contention with him. He was from Melina, that mysterious planet destroyed ages ago for its transgressions. He was ageless, timeless, deathless, waiting in some eternal limbo, ready for her when she was ready.

"You are very fortunate," I said, "to have somebody like Darios to do your writing."

She gave me a jaundiced look.

"I wouldn't jest about Darios."

She had a disconcerting way of reading my mind.

"Be a skeptic," she said, "that's why you were chosen. Oh, yes, you are an instrument, like myself, a warning light to prepare people for the coming calamity. But don't blind yourself to truth."

She gave me a piercing glance.

"Now how did Edgar Cayce say it would end?"

"He saw a tilting of the earth's rotational axis in 1936, gradually increasing until a resulting cataclysm would level our cities and mountains by the end of the century."

"Oh, it's coming, believe me, as I told you before. And man will help with his scientific discoveries, as he did once in Atlantis and Melina, and in our own solar system, with Mercury and Venus. Man never invented a weapon he didn't employ sooner or later, and just as the A-bomb was used to destroy Hiroshima and Nagasaki, so now will infinitely more destructive nuclear warheads be used in an unimaginable horror, causing the hills to crumble and the seas to wash over them.''

How much of this knowledge had gone into her books? I mentioned I had read a number of them with a view to their sources. She showed little interest.

"Did you feel you were Cornelia?" I asked.

She looked puzzled.

"Cornelia who?"

I explained where I had met the lady.

"Oh, pshaw," she said, "don't talk to me about that. How do we writers know what we have mixed together and where it all comes from?"

There was no further mention of the book she wanted from me, nor any hint as to why she had fastened on me. I had once thought it might have something to do with my interest in the psychic, but her experience was more extensive than my own. Besides, she regarded ESP—extrasensory perception—as a purely mechanistic function, which the animals had more of than ourselves.

"You worry too much," she said, with a smile, again reading my mind. "There's nobody I can speak to so candidly. Who else would listen seriously as I describe some of my weird experiences, which have far more implications than just ESP. For example, when I was sixteen, still unaware I had any special power, I was at a birthday party with a number of girls. Everybody was happy and gay, jabbering away as young girls do. Suddenly I saw a middle-aged man appear behind one of the girls. I saw his face as clearly as I see yours. He put his hand tenderly on her shoulder and bent down and kissed her cheek. She did not look at him, or show any awareness of his presence, and then I realized that I was up to my old tricks 'seeing things' again. I was upset that the girl didn't see him, for I knew they were close and that he had an urgent message for her. He was standing there so clearly, with the faintest aura about his head. Suddenly, he looked at me and smiled, and said:

"'I am glad that there is someone who sees me. Tell

Elizabeth that I've just left this world and came to say good-bye. Tell her to not weep for me. I am all right.''

Janet happened to look at a clock on the wall. It was eight o'clock.

She turned to the girl, knowing her father was dead, not knowing how to tell her. She finally asked, ''Elizabeth, is your father at home?''

''My father is out of town attending a meeting in New York. Why do you ask? You don't even know my father. Are you seeing things again?''

The others laughed, adding to Janet's embarrassment, but she persisted. ''Why don't you call home and find out if your father has called?''

Elizabeth uneasily made the call, then came back into the room laughing with obvious relief. ''Mom heard from Dad two hours ago. He was perfectly all right and will be home tomorrow.''

The girls resumed their carefree chattering, pointedly ignoring Janet for trying to cast a cloud over the party.

But the next day one of the girls rushed over to Janet's house and breathlessly announced, ''Elizabeth's father dropped dead last night in New York.''

''What time was it?'' Janet asked calmly.

''Eight o'clock.''

She was not surprised. Nor was she surprised that Elizabeth never spoke to her again. ''When we ran into each other, she looked at me with hatred. Somehow, she felt I was responsible for her father's death.''

It could have been a reassuring experience.

''If Elizabeth or her mother could have accepted what I saw, then she might have been heartened by the father's message. He was apparently in some state of survival and had wanted them not to grieve. If Marcus were to die before me, I think such a message would help me.''

I did not feel she was preening herself on her psychic powers. Rather, that she was seeking to exploit what gifts she had to explore the Unknown, to find some answer to the riddle of man's place in the universal scheme. What was so important about this tiny speck of dust in the unbelievably vast cosmos of billions of planets, in which a thousand Melinas could certainly exist without being known to man? With all our vaunted science, how little we knew of even our own history some six or seven thousand years into the past.

But still what evidence did she have. "What makes you so sure," I said, "that you have tuned into another planet with life on it?"

She let out a riotous laugh.

"What makes you think this contemptible little earth, this Terra with its greedy antlike creatures frantically crawling over each other to make a dollar, is the Creator's masterwork? I see Melina as clearly as I see ancient Rome and Greece, as I saw Florence, the Holy Land, and the cities and villages of Victorian England and America. They are more real to me than Los Angeles or New York."

And what connection did Melina have to Terra?

"It is a warning. Unfortunately, the proof is in the event. They were equally skeptical on Melina before its billions of people were destroyed. Only some six thousand survived. Even the Lord Darios could not save them." She suddenly sounded tired. "Believe me, it all happened before, out of the same arrogance and corruption we now find on Terra."

How curious that the human mind should be more fascinated with destruction than survival.

All I could ask was, "How was a whole planet wiped out?"

"God gave man the weapon, which could have been an instrument of good just as nuclear energy could be an agency of good. But he used it to destroy himself."

And how was this done?

"In the usual way. One nation warred on the other. Just as the Russians and the Chinese and the United States have the nuclear bomb, so the people of Melina had a weapon which suspended the time-space-matter continuum. Everything came to a standstill, the natural balance between oxygen and hydrogen, water and air, gases and solids. It was as if all of Melina was petrified. Thus, the supreme Creator who rules over even the Lord Darios obliterated the enormous cities, and all the vast tangle of roads and towers of learning.

"All that man made in folly was blown away, and again the forests and fields were gay with animal voices. The winds were no longer foul with pollution, the rivers ran clean and brilliant, and the oceans bubbled with new creation. There were no scars on the earth, no uglinesses that come from the souls of men. Melina was a new Eden—awaiting a new race of men."

Chapter Seven

MELINA MEETS TERRA

SHE had finally put Melina on the map. Her *Dialogues With the Devil*, featuring this distant planet in the boundless sky, was published by Doubleday in 1967. It did not create the stir she hoped, but it was provocative and promised to have a long life as its message of doom came ever closer to reality. People, Barker decided, didn't like being jarred out of their complacency.

Dialogues, as it was known, was the last of a metaphysical trilogy beginning with *The Listener* (1960) and continuing with *No One Hears But Him* (1966). The three books introduced the author to a new readership fascinated by the occult and the spiritual. They established her versatility and again brought into question her sources, for she would close her eyes and vast events would become transfigured as though by automatic writing. In her foreword was an acknowledgment the book was inspired by an alien presence, which took over midway in the book. Let the mockers have a field day at her expense. She, or rather the archangels Lucifer and Darios, had come to warn man he was tempting the gods. Who was he to think he could escape the fate of Venus and Mercury, and of Melina—all peopled once, but no longer.''

Melina, no ordinary star, but a satellite of Arcturus, had gone first, destroyed by its own rapaciousness. Its scientists had preened themselves on a method of halting all movement, but had not reckoned that their adversary, Predema, would turn this very weapon on them, just as other nations had taken America's nuclear bomb and were ready to use it. Life on Mercury, in our own solar system, was similarly destroyed when its orbit changed, just as the Earth's was changing, and it came too close to the sun. The sun then gave life to Venus, and it was her turn to move out of the darkness. But Venus, like Terra, couldn't abide peace and prosperity. Nations quarreled among themselves, and the ruling scientists applied the weapon of mass sterilization to their enemies, not realizing their own people would find it desirable as well. And then it was Terra's turn in the Sun, with God and His archangels tired of its transgressions. There was still a slim hope, if man would mend his ways, but Lucifer was delighted at the way things were working out. All the contending Darios could do was offer a refuge for the Biblical 144,000 souls to be returned to Melina, when the human cycle would be renewed, as from the time of Atlantis and before.

Barker had encouraged her ventures into the metaphysical, even though her historical and social novels were automatic best-sellers. I suspected he was something of a searcher himself. He had an easy familiarity with the New England transcendentalists led by Emerson, Thoreau, Hawthorne, and Bronson Alcott, and clearly felt there was more to life than death. He was forever intrigued, as were so many, by her constant references to medicine and surgery. But he had to become a surgical patient himself before fully appreciating passages from *Dear and Glorious Physician*, which he had glossed over before, particularly the scene in which the old surgeon Keptah showed the aspiring Luke his art.

"The picture of that girl on the operating table, her belly exposed to the knife, kept recurring while I was in the hospital," he recalled. "The scalpel drew a red streak across the ivory flesh, exposing the entrails. I remembered her description of the bladder—a great, gleaming bloody thing filled with corruption, sliding over the intestines, connected to the abdomen by a rope-like cord."

He had shaken his head, marveling. "And she had never witnessed an operation, nor read about one, regardless of the bibliography she tacked onto the book."

At this time, the spring of 1967, she was working on her *Testimony of Two Men*, a medical novel which dramatized the struggle of younger, idealistic doctors at the turn of the century to put the patients' interests ahead of a self-serving physicians' code that preached its infallibility while quietly burying its mistakes. It was a story of intrigue, passion, lust, and violence, the ingredients her readers had come to expect of her. And like the others, it became an instant best-seller. She was now a world-renowned figure. She liked to travel, visiting and revisiting the places she had visualized so brightly since childhood. She was drawn to the Holy Land, but felt strangely depressed when her steps took her to the central marketplace of Jerusalem and she followed Christ's weary steps to Calvary and the Cross.

We took our friendship for granted by this time, though I was still no clearer about her interest. She read nearly everything I wrote, especially in the occult. She had picked up *The Search for the Girl with the Blue Eyes*, but it had not sold her on its theme, reincarnation.

I had been impressed by my seventeen-year-old subject's recall of past lives under hypnosis, and together we had found the abandoned grave where she had presumably been buried and the remnants of a farmhouse where she had experienced the happiness and travails of a marriage mysteriously cut short by her husband's abrupt death. But, as I noted, her experience could have been attributed to flashes of extrasensory perception, with no basis in any previous existence. Janet saw this alternative as well.

She wrote from Buffalo in a dark mood. She had been hard at work on the Paul story, *Great Lion of God*, with book, as she put it, and was understandably depleted. The muse was flagging without the brilliant manifestations of light that marked her usual flights of fancy. And the purposelessness of life grew sharper as one drew closer to the grave. She had flirted with the notion of reincarnation, but now seemed concerned by its prospect.

"I read your book on reincarnation," she wrote, "and,

frankly, found it depressing, for I shudder at the very thought of being born again into this world. Life to me, practically from infanthood, has been a monstrous, painful, agonizing affair, and the idea of repeating such an existence—even if better, in a way—is horrifying to me. I think I'd prefer total oblivion. At least, as in sleep, you are safe from the revolting mechanics of living and being a prey 'to outrageous fortune.' It was bad enough when I was a very young child, a child, a teen-ager, a young woman, and then a mature woman. But life as one grows older daily becomes more intolerable in its bleakness, conformity, lightlessness, chrome-plated deadlines, and mechanism.

"It is also getting much more stupid. Stupidity—triumphant stupidity—seems endemic. On several occasions I have heard people in their forties, fifties, and sixties lyrically, and with excitement, remark on the 'brave new world' of the twenty-first century and its prophesied wonders, and they exclaim with a kind of euphoric hysteria, 'Oh, I can't wait!' At first I thought they were joking, but when I discovered they were not, I said, 'You won't need to wait. You just won't be alive then.' They look at me aghast and blink their eyes, and then do some slow and heavy mental mathematics, and then they are stricken."

Knowing this to be but a transitory mood, I wrote back encouragingly, pointing out that with her books she had contributed more than most and should take comfort in that. As I thought about it, my advice sounded pallid and cheerless. But she rejoined almost cheerfully with Omar Khayyam:

Ah, make the most of what we yet can spend,
Before we too into the dust descend,
Dust into dust, and under dust to lie
Sans song, sans wine, sans singer, and sans end.

I had moved to California, and it was not easy now to get together. But she phoned one day to say she was taking a brief holiday in New York, and could I meet her there. Marcus wasn't up to par, and she was joining Judy, who lived on Long Island, for another shopping spree and a round of parties.

"It always makes me feel better when I spend a lot of money," she wrote. "And, more importantly, there is something we must work out."

I was eager to see her and, if possible. to palliate her depression. But she was bright and animated, her eye sparkling, her conversation witty and sardonic. One would never know she had ever been depressed. She had just come in from a day of spending money, when I caught up to her at her hotel. She looked at Judy adoringly, than laid out the prizes she had acquired. Every imaginable gem was there—diamonds, rubies, emeralds, sapphires, even pearls, which she admired but considered commonplace.

I was looking at a fortune.

"Aren't you afraid of burglars?" I asked.

She shrugged. "What good are they locked up in a vault?"

Judy discovered things she had to do and thoughtfully went off to her room.

Janet's eyes followed her out the door. "What a wonderful girl," she said, "and such a joy."

She turned her full gaze on me and gave me an unusually probing look.

"You men are so horrible," she said. "You never seem to age. I guess it's shaving that does it."

She poured her coffee and lit a cigarette, and again turned her eyes on me. "Now don't get alarmed," she said, "but I have been picking up on you."

"Don't tell me," I groaned, "I don't want to know."

She went on anyway, as I wondered whether I had been brought three thousand miles for a psychic reading I didn't want.

"I find something rather uncomfortable in your pelvic region," she said, "and I suggest a chiropractor, not an authentic M.D. Something is bothering you emotionally, too, and you are uncertain about someone's reactions to you. I say the hell with it. There are more fish in the sea.''

She looked at me closely, satisfied that she had scored a hit. ''And don't accept less money for something which you know is worth much more. You will get the larger sum if you hold out.''

I had been dickering with Doubleday on a new book and wondered if she had been talking to Barker. She again read my mind. ''I have not discussed it with anybody,'' she said.

She now got into an occult area which I had not thought she took seriously, save for that remarkable experience with the Reverend Nicholson in Buffalo, and her own apparent communication with the girl's father who had just died, which of course could have been a dramatization of her own subconscious and a purely clairvoyant experience.

''I 'hear' someone near you, a very close male friend to whom you were attached in the past,'' she went on. ''He thinks you are now doing something which is not worthy of your talents. And there's a woman around you whom he does not like at all. Your loneliness, he says, is not something new to you, but almost from birth, and you just have to accept it in a very mediocre world. Also, you are considering quite an unusual novel, and he wants you to begin it, for it will be very successful. He also wants you to forgive someone now dead who did you a great injury, which you can't forget because it truly caused you a trauma. The future is much brighter for you than you realize at just this point—and watch out for that woman.''

She broke off suddenly.

''Now don't think I am prying, but you should get rid of that girl. She's a leech.''

I quickly went over what she had said. Actually, I had developed a sacroiliac condition and had thought of consulting a chiropractor. I had mixed feelings about a young woman, but who didn't? I was contemplating a novel, which Lee Barker wanted me to write, but had no idea if I could manage it. She hit the mark on the deceased person, but I had gotten over that, I thought. I wasn't sure that I believed in her spirits, feeling, as I said, that she was dramatizing her own sub-conscious impressions. But who could say? She picked out my dead brother and grandmother by name, imputing certain con-versations and concerns to them which seemed natural. But what intrigued me most was why she was saying all this.

I looked up to catch her smile.

"Is this why you sent for me?" I asked.

She shook her head. "You need direction. You are to do great things, with me and alone. We have several projects together, and you shall go on to writing novels and screenplays."

I felt a quick pang of guilt.

"I haven't got anywhere on our book. I just don't know where to begin."

"I think it should be on the metaphysical," she said. "That way it would reflect my thinking, rather than my pedigree. Who cares about who was the tenth Earl of Nothing?"

It was difficult, as Lee Barker had pointed out, to begin a book before you knew how to end it. Or even knew the middle, for that matter.

"It will come to you," she said, as I wondered anew why she was so keen on my working with her, when the world was crowded with writers who would have jumped at the chance.

"What do you think of *déjà vu*?" she said, cutting short my thought.

I shook my shoulders. "I guess we've all had the ex-perience of being somewhere or meeting somebody strange we have a feeling of familiarity with. Why do you ask?"

She gave me a sharp glance.

"Have you ever considered you knew me before?"

I grinned. "Not in this life."

She smiled enigmatically.

"Think about it. And maybe the book will come a lot easier."

Chapter Eight

THE FATAL ATTACK

LEE Barker obviously wasn't himself. His voice was uncharacteristically high-pitched, and there was a quiver of excitement in it.

"Something terrible has happened," he exclaimed over an exasperatingly noisy long-distance line, "Janet and Marcus have been brutally attacked in their home. Janet was beaten on the head and is in a daze. Marcus was knocked unconscious and is in terrible shape. He may not recover."

Only the night before they had been unfortunate enough to surprise two burglars ransacking their bedroom. They were knocked down and mercilessly pummeled, bound and gagged, held hostage while the robbers leisurely combed over their belongings, somehow missing most of the jewelry.

Janet had managed to loosen her bonds a few minutes after they left and had then freed Marcus. With the servants off for the night, she had called for help. Marcus was taken in a semicoma to the hospital. Though she came off better, the beating had affected Janet's hearing and eyesight and left her hysterical. But at sixty-seven, ten years Marcus's junior, she was far more vigorous and had a better chance of it.

There was no clue to the robbers as yet, though an aroused and bandaged Janet swore she could pick them out in the black hole of Calcutta on a starless night.

Barker had cancelled all his appointments and planned to leave for Buffalo at once.

"In the midst of all the confusion," he said, "she wanted you to know about it. She'll write as soon as her head stops throbbing and she can sit up at the typewriter.''

There had not only been a traumatic shock from the mauling she and Marcus took, but the jarring realization that with all her fame and fortune, she had no privacy and no immunity from the street. Anybody could walk in and kill anybody at any time, and most likely suffer few or no consequences.

I promptly put in a call, but she could not come to the phone. She could not have heard anyway. Marcus was due for a long stay in the hospital, and she was up in a few days, attending him around the clock. Fortunately, she had the constitution of her Irish grandparents and was functioning, though painfully and a little bleary-eyed. Her major concern was Marcus, who, at seventy-seven, had gone into baffling complications. When she finally wrote, weeks after the attack, she appeared obsessed with the inability of the doctors to arrive at some diagnosis, a dereliction she had been dealing with in her *Testimony of Two Men*, now near completion.

"Marcus," she wrote, "is in critical condition. He has been in and out of the hospital and growing thinner and paler and more despondent every day. No one seems to know what is the matter! They have actually tested him for tropical diseases though he hasn't been in the tropics since 1950, including undulant fever, ague, black water fever, and sundry other exotic things with the exception of yaws. Malaria was ruled out. He seems to get well, gains a little weight at home, then suddenly is shaken by the most incredible chills for half an hour, followed by at least six degrees of fever, then passes out unconscious. At this point the meat-wagon comes for the poor dear—again—and he is hauled off to the hospital, where antibiotics and baths and whatnot immediately cool down the fever. He is very weak, loses all the weight he gains and then some, is discharged, comes home, and the whole cycle is repeated over and over and over again. They say SOME infection hits him, but what it is they do not know. They do know that it caused him to have double bronchial and lobar pneumonia, as a sort of playful little touch, and then it hit his liver and pancreas. I wish to God Edgar Cayce were still alive. Perhaps he could make a diagnosis and recommend a cure, as he did for so many people. The baffled doctors even took a very painful encephalogram last week and dejectedly reported that his brain waves were 'perfect.' They tested him for cancer in practically every organ and found everything normal. The only thing they didn't test him for was pregnancy. This has been going on for month after month. I don't think doctors know very much. So far, we have paid out over $27,000 for their idiot researches on him.

"You won't believe this, but they triumphantly reported some 'odd growths in his stomach, cauliflower shaped,' and took more and more X-rays, then suddenly the 'growths' were gone. They were baffled. I told them that he had been eating mustard cauliflower pickles at home—and then I heard no more rumors about 'growths.' The more I see and hear of doctors, the more apprehensive I get. I do have a theory about what he has, but no one listens to me. I think his struggles with the armed thugs injured his spine and that nerves are being pinched—but the doctors laugh.''

Marcus had been a vital cog in her life. In her desire to draw him into the mainstream of her activity, she had delegated bits and pieces of research to him and even encouraged the belief that he did some of the writing. A genuine affection had grown between them over the years, bred of her conviction that he was her soulmate, destined even before birth to be her husband. He tolerated this view of himself, though he didn't quite accept it, and they stuck through some hard knocks together. She freely acknowledged that she needed a man around the house, somebody that made her feel like a woman. He had been a reassuring presence, if only to be ignored. He was a buffer between her and a demanding public, and though inexpert, he took the burden of publishers and agents off her hands. He dealt with the lawyers, tradespeople, and the curious. Sometimes he exceeded her wishes, keeping her from people she enjoyed seeing, and this led to disharmonies, which she enjoyed because resolving them cleared the air. Since the attack, however, there was little he could do. He had been hopelessly bedridden, wasting away, more vegetable than human, when he finally died on August 13, 1970, in a Buffalo hospital.

The three years of dying had been a terrible trial. Watching him shrink away before her eyes, insensibly losing his vital functions, she would slip to her knees and pray that he would soon be spared his suffering, "I ask nothing for myself, God, only for dear Marcus."

The last enemy to be conquered was death. But she saw no sign of triumph, only a degrading, ignominious loss of dignity. Dying seemed even worse than death itself, for it made a mockery of all the hopes and dreams man nourished in the bud and bloom of life. What had been sweet and sentimental was crushed by the unspeakable cruelty of a mocking old age and a senseless death. In Marcus's last travail, she saw once more man's ultimate fate. Was she talking into the wind when she cried out to God? Was anybody listening? Did anybody care? Or was there only nothingness?

She had written death scenes like this so often, and they had been real and poignant, experienced to a point where she had suffered with her characters. But an end had come when the book was done and put away. Now there was no end to the grief and sense of loss. It was a bottomless void. And in this void the thought kept dinning at her: What was the purpose of it all? For every moment of joy there was a penalty of pain. Why? Why were we here and why did we suffer? From childhood she had heard the homily that we grow through adversity, but she found it fatuous, for what did we grow to but the grave?

Undoubtedly, being alone after forty years of marriage had much to do with her pessimism. But, essentially, the fundamental question lay out there unanswered. Had God turned his back on his creatures—if there was a God? Was it all a cruel hoax, a Creation by accident, without design or meaning? If there was some universal intelligence, some higher force, then what, if anything, was wanted of man? Was he given life to struggle fitfully with his empty dreams, then perish in trembling oblivion?

In her despair and fatigue, she gave way to a mood of dark surrender.

"Now," she wrote, "the thought of eternal death is like a balm—and the dearest hope. It is not 'melancholy' over my husband's dreadful and mysterious illness that colors my hope. It is just that my whole life has been one almost interminable dreadfulness and despair from the moment I can remember, with practically no light or joy or peace in it.

"Even my memories of the past—if they are memories, indeed—were all one piece with despair and terror, hopelessness and pain and gloom. I haven't a single happy 'memory,' not one, nor of peace. I don't know whether I believe in them or not, but I hope they are, indeed, only dreams and not realities. 'Happy is the day of one's death,' said Job. Amen. If I was supposed to learn something, I sure haven't learned anything except that life is torment and the end of it is the best. It seems to me that I was more aware, more adult and more mature—and more knowledgeable and educated—in former 'lives' than I am now, and braver, and that, if anything, I have declined in them all."

With time, her pain seemed to ease and she appeared to renew her interest in an extra dimension of life which she somehow associated with the Lord Darios and his archangels. They were very tangible and real beings to her. She felt I could not write about her without writing about Darios, and yet she cautioned: "Darios is a very wrathful archangel, with a bad and violent temper and a harsh disposition. It is possible he would stop at nothing if offended."

She had new sobering thoughts about *The Search for the Girl with the Blue Eyes*, having reread it in her veiled quest for some clue to an afterlife.

"You went about the search with the clear calm eye of a scientist. Had it been sentimental and zealous it would have lost its magic and aroused skepticism. You did not succumb to the lure of romanticism and play down doubts. In fact, there were moments of sharp cynicism which I deeply appreciated.''

Her interest in the Unknown had been quickened by a curious incident which occurred only a few hours after Marcus was buried, but which she had not been ready to discuss until now.

"On his deathbed," she said, "Marcus came out of his coma long enough to reach out and take my hand and whisper:

"'If there is life after death, I will come back and give you a sign.'"

Three days after his death, she had been alone in her room, half-heartedly thinking of this, when her housekeeper burst in on her and excitedly summoned her to the backyard. "You must come," she cried, "it is a miracle!"

She crawled downstairs, where a strange and unsettling phenomenon greeted her. There, in the garden back of the house, on the afternoon of his funeral, a clump of Resurrection Lilies, which had not bloomed for twenty years, was blossoming in full glory.

She could not believe her eyes. She pinched herself, remembering how Marcus for years had joked about the bush, which he had planted himself, saying, "You can't prove the Resurrection by these lilies."

Only the day before the gardener had wanted to dig out the bush. For no particular reason she had demurred, and now she knew why. (The lilies resembled Madonna Lilies and had a similar fragrance.)

"Every flower was in bloom," she said. "There must have been fifteen or sixteen of them."

Now from her own examination of the Apostle Paul she drew the obvious parallel.

"Don't you remember Paul saying of Christ's death and Ressurrection that if one man lived then all lived, for why else had Christ died but to prove life everlasting?"

It was a reassuring omen, in a way, and she badly needed somebody, even it it was only a ghost.

"It would be comforting to know that Marcus was about," she said. "He was much to skeptical to be a believer.

But he did wonder about the alternatives, as death drew close."

She wrote more often now since she could no longer hear on the phone. She compensated by reading lips, a practice she had become adept at when Marcus's voice had become so weak she had to strain to hear him. She had made another and more exciting discovery. She could pick up his thoughts anytime he mentally expressed a need. And she worked at this for a while, finding she could pick up on some others as well, though not on the telephone.

But deafness was still a maddening frustration, as she found she could only "hear" people she was attuned to emotionally. "For the most part I hear sounds as loud as other people, but I cannot interpret them. It is a hopeless jumble. When most people speak to me it is as if they are speaking a foreign language. Ear specialists offer no help, telling me to smile and nod amiably when spoken to, since nine-tenths of what people say is not worth listening to."

Smiling and nodding had cost her dearly. "When I find my finances are in terrible shape, the bankers, agents, and business managers say to me, 'But you smiled and nodded.'"

By this time we were old friends, and I scarcely wondered why we had become friends. She seemed to delight in oblique references to some obscure debt I owed her, and likewise her obligations to me. I had no idea what this was all about. But she was very positive. And, surprisingly or not, she did listen to me. I encouraged her to resume writing, and travel, pointing out that Jesus enjoined the grief-stricken to let the dead bury the dead. And so I was pleased when she announced she would be putting aside the black crepe and traveling to South Africa for a holiday with her new companion-business manager, Jan Robinson, wife of a prominent Buffalo judge whom she had known since he was a boy.

Her trip was a grand success. As a guest of the South African government, she was feted like royalty, whisked around the countryside from Cape Town to Durban, interviewed at every little way station, honored by the nation's writers, including Stuart Cloete. At one hotel, where the royal suite had been set aside, the authorities made the same mistake I had. They had been looking for a male Taylor Caldwell, and when Jan Robinson checked in, the management promptly assigned the two to tiny "wall-closet" rooms with a view of a dingy courtyard. The mistake was soon discovered, when local dignitaries came to pick up their celebrated visitor and were brightly informed by a desk clerk that "Mister Caldwell" had not yet arrived. Nothing fazed Janet; she gave a memorable speech, which her hosts found heartwarming in light of the unjustified criticism they felt apartheid was receiving abroad. She was shown native settlements, housing developments, schools, all vastly superior, she felt, to the slums in which blacks were jammed together in America, and spoke to natives, who expressed surprise at being objects of sympathy abroad. She came away from South Africa impressed by its people, black and white.

Back in the States, she leaped with fresh enthusiasm into her "Kennedy book," *Captains and the Kings*, taking an occasional break to meet with Barker in New York. My first novel, *The Reporter*, which she had predicted, was out at this time and was not doing as well as I had hoped. She was very encouraging. I had come to New York to discuss an astrology book with another publisher, and we three, Barker, Janet and myself, had inevitably gotten together. Barker had no objections to my publishing one book elsewhere. "Doubleday doesn't do everything right," he said, with a glance for Janet, "but we're still better than anybody else, as you will find out."

"Oh, you'll be back with Doubleday," said Janet, "with a book I have in mind for you."

I assumed she was speaking about "our book," which I still had made no headway with, and with which, frankly, she had been no help.

She was dealing now with life on her terms. She spoke less of Darios and more of Paddy, whom she pictured as a charming Irish Lothario from County Kerry. They had apparently met on the trip, and his wit had captivated her. The attraction was mutual. He had a castle in Killarney and wanted to whisk her there on an emerald carpet the moment she gave the word. Marcus was not forgotten, only displaced for the time by this paragon. "You will meet him when you come to Buffalo," she said. "He will be visiting me there. Better bring your woolies, for the snow season will have begun by then. I think you will like Paddy, for all that he is a free-drinking bellicose Irishman and a peer."

There was nothing, apparently, that Paddy couldn't do.

"He skis, plays golf and tennis, ice skates, climbs mountains, swims like a shark, can dance all night, and thinks Protestants are hell's brew [clearly a Catholic]. He was educated at Eton and Oxford and can be charming—until he drinks. We are always fighting. He has a chalet in Switzerland and houses all over the world, and for some mysterious reason he wants to marry me and insists I give up my writing. I want neither. He is sixty and has a mistress in every city, I believe, and two illegitimate children. Paddy-O is quite a man."

She never told the same story twice. At one point he was single and eligible, at another he had an insanely jealous wife. I supposed it made little difference, but it was confusing.

"Why do wives have to be so possessive?" she complained, with a toss of her head. "Since Marcus died I have given parties for my gentlemen friends in Buffalo. No women allowed, of course. And the men love it; they just sit back, raise up their feet, and drink and talk as they can't do around these wives. The wives hate me, of course. They can't imagine their husbands enjoying themselves away from them, when, as a matter of fact, they don't enjoy a moment with them. All these wives talk about is household chores and children. Don't they know men want to forget the children? They're such babies themselves."

Two men had insulted her horribly within the last month and were off her list. "One said I had a beautiful soul and a tremendous mind. The other—worse—said I was the only intellectual woman he had ever met. Now if they had said something about my complexion, which is excellent, and my figure, which isn't at all bad, or my legs, which are there with the best, I'd have been delighted. But no woman was ever 'intellectual,' and no woman really ever amounted to anything in the genius line. Where are our Michelangelos, our Beethovens, our Wagners, our Ibsens, our Shakespeares?''

Paddy wouldn't have anything to do with her salons. He preferred seeing her alone, at which times he would read from poetry he had written her, or recite from Keats, Shelly, and Byron, while she came back with Shakespeare, Swinburne, and Kipling. All in all, a wonderful romantic idyll.

I had been looking forward to meeting this free-booting swashbuckler, but she sadly reported a wrinkle in the romance. Paddy had called off the trip to Buffalo and sent an ultimatum. "He tells me I am to give up my writing and be the Lady of the Manor, or it is all off.'' We were alone now at her hotel, but she looked over her shoulder as if to make sure she was not being overheard. She was vacillating. "I can't bear to part with the Boyfriend—who is quite a hunk of man—and I can't give up my writing, which I have pursued since I was six and which is my life. Worst of all, if I say no to him I will have to return his jewelry, and I adore jewelry after perfume and pretty underwear.''

At present he was cruising on his huge yacht, taking over the helm during rough weather, but he was never too busy to handle pressing ventures on the ship-to-shore phone. Clearly cast in the heroic mold, he could have stepped out of a Taylor Caldwell novel. She loved talking about him.

"They don't make men like Paddy anymore,'' she said, "he's a throwback to the last century, a gay, rollicking predator, gallant and chivalrous, yet ribbed with steel.'' She gave me an imploring look. "What should I do?''

I took Paddy-O at her word.

"Play hard to get,'' I said.

"Play games at my age, never.'' She sighed. "I know in these days of Women's Lib a woman should not be preoccupied with pleasing a man. I should be manly and dominant, wear slacks to dinner, and call you delightful men chauvinistic male pigs. But I like fraternizing with the enemy. It has delightful compensations. But what am I to do with Paddy?''

The whole thing had happened so suddenly that it hardly seemed real. As I thought of it, I found it hard to put a finger on this phantomlike character. He didn't have much tangibility, just a first name, a place in Ireland, a yacht, and a surprising desire to get tangled up with a woman who could dominate any male by virtue of her strongmindedness and celebrity.

A few days later I visited her in Buffalo, to discuss ''our book'' and meet with the ephemeral Paddy, who had reinstated his visit. By this time she had added another financial adviser, liking men around, and this worthy was very much concerned about the rollicking Irish peer, though, like myself, he had never seen him.

''Who is this Paddy?'' he asked, with a worried frown. ''He keeps wiring Janet that she shouldn't trust a soul, especially me.''

Apparently, Paddy was bombarding her with suspicions of the people around her. She had shown this adviser one letter, which he now showed me. He was bemoaning Paddy's officiousness when an elegantly gowned Janet walked into the room and immediately spotted the letter.

''I see you two have been talking about Paddy,'' she said with a pleased smile. She waved her arm, and a bracelet of rubies glittered on her wrist. ''Just something Paddy gave me,'' she said.

Her adviser's eyes boggled.

''Paddy gave you that?''

Her voice rose a little.

''And why not, may I ask?''

She turned to me with an air of concern. ''Should I meet Paddy in London, unchaperoned?''

''But I thought he was coming here.''

She shrugged. ''You know these tycoons.''

At their ages, I thought they could meet anywhere, unchaperoned, but all I said was, ''Do whatever pleases you.''

That evening, after the guests had left and the housekeeper had retired, we sat in her kitchen over a pot of coffee, and she produced an envelope postmarked from somewhere overseas. She carefully extracted the letter and handed it to me. It was beautifully written. Taylor Caldwell could have done no better. And in no uncertain terms it expressed Paddy's affection for his lady love.

"He wants me to fly off with him," she said, adding archly, "don't you think we're much too old to elope?"

"You mentioned he was married," I said.

She looked startled, but only for a moment.

"Well, people do get divorced."

She gave me an inquiring glance.

"What do you think of him?"

"I've never met him."

She clicked her teeth impatiently. "Of course you have, at a dinner party in New York. He was the most distinguished figure there."

I could not place him. Still, Paddy excited my curiosity. He had come out of nowhere to usurp Darios as a major topic of discussion. And now, without a single appearance, was having an agitating effect on her household.

She slipped on her reading glasses and took another letter from her bag. "This is from the adviser you just met. He can't stand Paddy."

I looked up in surprise.

"Why did he write?"

"So I can pass it on to Paddy. I had asked Paddy about him, and he told me not to trust anybody, particularly people who want to invest my money."

I quickly ran through the note. It had an aggrieved tone but was conciliatory.

"I read Paddy's letter, but rather than take offense," it went, "I quite agree with most of what he says. So when he tells you not even to trust me, it is due to not really knowing me. My initial reaction was to feel hurt that he would feel this way. However, after thinking about it, I realize he could not logically tell you to trust me when he doesn't know me that well. But I feel that I have fulfilled my promise to you and Paddy to protect and shield you at all times."

With a cryptic smile she pushed the letter back into her bag.

"A woman," she said, "needs a strong man at her side to defend her against vultures."

"And you have Paddy."

She smiled serenely.

"He has warned me about you as well."

I looked back into her eyes and smiled. And then, suddenly, it hit me and I laughed to myself. Of course I knew Paddy. I had met him in a dozen Taylor Caldwell novels. He was the perfect answer to a lonely woman's dream.

Chapter Nine

REINCARNATION?

STILL fascinated by the Unknown, she kept probing the possibility of continuing life, while deprecating any personal interest in reincarnation. I had the feeling she wanted to believe, but was deterred by the absence of anything but the most circumstantial evidence. Again she brought up *The Search for the Girl with the Blue Eyes*, in which hypnotist Joe Lampl had regressed the seventeen-year-old Canadian girl who claimed to have lived many times before.

"How do you know that anything you say under hypnosis is true?" she said.

"You don't, I suppose, without checking it, though there's a good deal of emotion in the course of a regression that can hardly be faked."

"I don't quite understand reincarnation," she said. "You aren't the same person, you don't have the same consciousness, so you are not you. You are somebody else with somebody else's personality—but you are not you. It is worse than hearing a father say his children are his immortality. But—they are not him." She shook her head. "When somebody comes back from the other side and tells me about it, then I'll know there's something to it."

"How about the lilies that bloomed in your yard?

"Oh, that," she said. "I needed that, and it did give me a lift. But let's face it, what did it prove?" Only what I wanted to put into it. I've adjusted and don't need to fool myself. Don't think I've forgotten Marcus. But when a thing is over, it is over. Period. No repinings—at least not much. Don't you love people who talk about happy memories? I don't give a damn for them. I am too eager to see what the future—the near future—will bring, and the hell with the past."

She was very much her old self now, having renewed her zest for living, with travel and new friends. But it was her writing that restored her spirits and gave her some shred of purpose, some reason for existence on this earthly plane. She no longer wrote for money; she had more money than she could ever hope to spend, but felt compelled to write, as though in probing her own mind for the scenes and situations, the mystique and metaphysics she thrust into her books, she would stumble on some explanation of her own being. She had just finished *Captains and the Kings* and was pleased with it, having deliberately kept it free of her metaphysical interest.

"*Captains and the Kings* gets me out of the metaphysical and down to earth. There's nothing spiritual about it. It deals with a tough Irishman who got rich hook or crook, then pulled strings to make his son President." She had smiled archly. "Any reference to old Joe Kennedy is strictly incidental."

This book was to add to her fame, but it was not at the core of her thinking. What had it to do with Darios or Michael or Lucifer or any of the luminous voices she heard in the night? If the attainment of power was man's purpose, how ephemeral all life was. Had not a mighty Persian monarch gazed down at his triumphant host, then burst into tears lamenting that in a few scant years everyone on that field of glory would be dead, never having known why they lived?

As we spoke together, I considered things we would have once thought impossibilities.

"What would the Victorians have thought about flights to the moon, space craft, airplanes, television, the telephone, computers, even the transister radio, which magically brings music and voices through brick and cement?"

She gave me a frosty look.

"That has nothing to do with immortality."

"But it does show that something can exist without our understanding it. How about the cities you have seen and the events you have recalled? Are they less substantial because we don't understand why you saw them?"

She grimaced. "Oh, you journalists, always trying to trip up a person."

She had not spoken of Darios or Melina for a while.

"Has Darios stopped coming to you?"

She stared out a window.

"He will always be there. But I'm not sure I can say the same for myself."

Her eyes turned back to me, and she frowned.

"In your research into the psychic," she said, "have you thought that if the future can be predicted, which happens all the time, then that future is out there waiting for every one of us, president or pauper, leaving us little or no free will, no matter what we believe?"

"Yes, I have thought of all that," I said, "and have decided the way we react to events eventually determines our happiness or unhappiness."

She nodded solemnly.

"If the future is fixed, then the past must have been fixed as well, for it was once the future. Is that not so?"

I failed to see what she was getting at.

"If you were to regress me," she explained, "perhaps we would get at the truth of the past, and then, and only then, know with absolute certainty that what we foresee for the future is also true. For it must all come out of the same bottle."

She still had a disconcerting way of reading my thoughts. "This is still not the book I saw for us," she said. And then, suddenly, she took on that faraway look I was to know so well, and she quoted softly from Kipling:

> *When Earth's last picture is painted,*
> *And the tubes are twisted and dried.*
> *When the oldest colors have faded, and*
> *The youngest critic has died,*
> *We shall rest, and, faith, we shall need*

> *It—lie down for an eon or two,*
> *Till the Master of All Good Workmen*
> *Shall put us to work anew.*

On this note, I returned to California to ponder my connection with this unpredictable woman who had the distinction of being the most popular woman author in America.

She was a woman full of paradoxes, and even this was a paradox. For the metaphysical and the material were happily joined in her. Nobody could command a greater price for a book yet to be written. And this brought out still another paradox. Offered sums up to a million dollars to write any novel that suited her fancy, she clung loyally to Barker and Doubleday, taking any advance payment they offered. By this time she had no concern about money, for it was continually flowing in, not only from this country but from countries all over the world. She was as popular in Germany and France, and in her native England, as she was in the States. Even her old books added to her wealth, constantly reprinted for sums far greater than she had received originally. Paperback rights for *The Arm and the Darkness*, first published in 1943, brought $350,000 for a book thirty years old. And yet, poor as she had been, she had no intrinsic love of money, leaving its handling to banks and business agents, caring only that there was enough for anything she wanted.

There was greater game afoot. After teetering uncertainly on the brink of the Unknown, she was now ready to plunge headlong into the wilderness. I hadn't been home a week before Barker called. His voice rang with enthusiasm. Janet had offered to come out to California and submit to a hypnotic regression that might account for her remarkable knowledge of ancient history, religion, railroads, banking, munitions, medicine, finance, steel, and politics, and any other subject that crept into her books—even to Creation itself.

From her writing, Barker wasn't quite sure how she stood on reincarnation—or God. "She's a Catholic, born a Protestant, and was married to a Jew. That certainly covers the field."

At last we both knew what she wanted of me. This would resolve, once and for all, any lingering doubts she had about reincarnation. Oddly, I felt an anticlimactic sense of disappointment, for at most how could this book be anything but a variation of *The Search for the Girl with Blue Eyes*? I had expected more. As it turned out, my first feeling was the correct one.

She liked the idea of being regressed, dipping deeply into her subconscious under hypnosis, hoping to clarify her own sources, including the redoubtable Darios. His appearances were now infrequent. He had come to her during Marcus's illness and announced, as she was grieving, "Your husband is going to die, but God will not give you the shock of a sudden separation."

He had appeared again after Marcus's death, but she preferred not to discuss it. "He doesn't like me gossiping," she explained.

I wondered now whether *Dear and Glorious Physician*, *Great Lion of God*, *Testimony of Two Men*, or any of the other novels had come from Darios. Who had told her of Paul's red hair and blue eyes, of Luke's meeting with Mary, the mother of Jesus, and of the incredible surgery of Keptah, the physician?

I looked forward to her arrival. Jan Robinson, a pleasant, attractive lady of fifty or so, who was still with her, had been sent on ahead because she had a cold and Janet didn't want to take a chance of catching it. Janet came on the next day and I met her at the airport.

She emerged from the plane, blinking into the unaccustomed sun, and greeted me with a warm embrace. And then, with a sweeping gesture, she handed me a frazzled-looking brown paper bag.

I peered into the bag and saw a dazzling collection of emeralds, diamonds, rubies, and other precious stones. They were easily worth two million dollars.

She caught my look of astonishment.

"Why own them if you can't wear them? But I'm getting rid of them after this trip. It gives people ideas."

The porter came along with a cart full of bags and heaped them on the airport walk. She had enough luggage for a six-month holiday.

"You're only going to be here two weeks," I said, wondering how I could fit it all into my car.

She gave my battered Mustang a jaundiced look. "Is that your manservant's?"

Then she looked around over her shoulder.

"Where is Jan?" she said. "I hope she's gotten over her sniffles. I don't want to get anything I didn't have the pleasure of catching."

"Jan's at the hotel, getting things ready. The California sunshine has cured her cold."

She shivered in the warm sunlight. "It's worse than Buffalo," she said.

That evening we had a rather listless dinner, both Jan and Janet still feeling the effects of jet lag, but Janet grabbed the bill, as always, with her usual, "It's on me. You're both deductible."

The next day the sessions began. As she was almost somnambulistic, Janet was a good subject. Because of her deafness, cards were made out with the questions. She glanced at them under hypnosis, with the curious ambivalence people have while hypnotized. I had decided on daylong sessions for as long as Jane would put up with them. She was told nothing of what she was saying, to keep her subconscious mind from being influenced by what she had already said. It soon became obvious the cards weren't necessary. In the subconscious state, which she was often in anyway, she was able to pick up my thoughts with ease. We took her back in time, at ten-year intervals, from her marriage to Marcus back to first husband Bill Combs. And as far as we knew everything was factual. Her voice changed with every time sequence, and she was always cold.

The years dwindled down. At five, she was living in England, going to school in Manchester, and her life was a fright. "I spilled a bottle of ink on my white pinafore. I didn't dare go home with ink on my pinafore. The teacher said,

'Your mother wouldn't kill you just because you have ink on your pinafore!' I said yes she would, because she was always saying she was going to kill me because she didn't want children anymore.''

Pathetic, but still not unusual, and then out of a two-year-old's memory bank came a cry that stirred my attention. The child Taylor lay huddled in her bed, and then, as her heart froze, the bedroom door opened a crack. She sat up, petrified. "He"—in a small-child's voice—"he came in with two great lions on each side of him. All gold and silver tips on their manes. He called me by name and said, 'They will always protect you.' Then he said, 'You should not have come back, but you persist.' "

Not come back? From where, and to what, and by whose doing? It was an enigma on top of a riddle. Could this be the Presence she had spoken of, the incandescent visitor from Melina? Was it he, Darios, whose name I dared not speak?

She sighed and slipped away, responding to no further questions.

Resting briefly between sessions, she sat around my sun-drenched living-room, looking out on the Pacific, and complained of the lack of central heating. "It makes Buffalo a summer resort," she grumbled. Neither Jan Robinson nor I was in the least cold, and the temperatures ranged in the sixties.

She didn't like not being told what she had been saying. "I'm doing all this to find out where I'm at," she said, "and you're keeping it a secret from me, while telling the rest of the world about it."

"That's not quite accurate," said Jan Robinson, "for you will have a complete report of everything you experienced before anybody else does."

Even though she didn't know what was going on, she enjoyed being regressed. Under hypnosis she was even more clairvoyant than normal, for her subconscious became a clear channel unobstructed by conscious thought. Each time period was chosen in relationship to her writing. We regressed her to the 1800s, the Victorian period, the setting for so many of her books, the age of Swinburne, George Eliot, Kipling, and others she was so knowledgeable about. She had once said with a half-mocking smile that if she was anybody from the past it would most likely be George Eliot, the Victorian novelist whose work she was so familiar with. "I even know where she had writing blocks," she said.

This provided some comedy relief, for under hypnosis she was an Irish scullery maid named Jeannie McGill, and she toiled for George Eliot—Mary Ann Evans—in both London and Warwickshire. Since she could neither read nor write, how could she have remembered *The Mill on the Floss* and other books by George Eliot? A reassuring explanation soon offered itself. The author, like so many writers, tested her prose on whoever was handy. The little maidservant was a captive audience. And the subconscious, we knew, was an infallible storehouse of the memory.

"Could it be," I whispered over Janet's prone body, "that this is a carryover from another life?"

Jan Robinson shrugged, not believing in reincarnation. "Beats me."

And that was my reaction as well.

As Jeannie, she had a short and unhappy life. Wrongly accused of stealing, she was flung into prison. There, she was cold and forlorn and friendless.

Forgotten by her mistress, who was sunning herself in Italy, she abandoned all hope and hanged herself in her cell. She was sixteen.

Janet sobbed through this story, tears streaming down her cheeks, then sat up with a puzzled look and demanded: "What the hell am I crying about?"

She regarded me suspiciously. "I don't know what you're doing to me. I feel like two different people."

In her most recent life experience, as the English seamstress Wilma Sims, she had died in 1898, two years before her present birth on September 7, 1900. We decided to probe the brief period between the end of one life and the beginning of another, to see what, if anything, she saw after death.

I looked at her eyes: they were closed, and her face was composed. She could have been sleeping.

"Where did your soul go after you died?" I asked.

"Melina," she said, sending a tiny chill up my spine. "I stayed at home in Melina for a while. I was happy, very happy."

And there she was rejoined not only with Darios, but saw the archangels Michael and Lucifer, who viewed her with displeasure because, as a mere mortal, she had dared to entice one of their own.

"Why did you leave Melina and come back to earth again?"

"I had to rejoin Marcus. He was my soulmate."

He had spurned her when she was Wilma Sims—a name she had vaguely recalled earlier as Willie or Millie—and failed her when she was a nun, and so he had the opportunity now to redress these wrongs.

"Estanbul [Marcus] was already born, appearing on this earth again eleven years before I died [1887 was Marcus Reback's birth year]. He was born in Russia. I did not know this until I went home to Melina. I thought I had been responsible for Estanbul's exile. One does not offend the Lord Darios."

She had loved Estanbul, but not as she did Darios. "I thought I could help Estanbul, and with my love he would never need to be born again. Then he could return to his home in Melina. But it was all delusion. He never did love me, all through the endless lives."

She had other lives, but she nearly always was a poor thing, cold and hungry, ravaged by men, abused by women, haunted by fate. Estanbul, as the priest Francisco, had betrayed her in another very inconsequential life. Indeed, they never seemed to fulfil each other, and so had to try again.

Much of this was in *The Search for a Soul*, *The Psychic Lives of Taylor Caldwell*, published in 1973. But as I look back after seven years, I see a number of logical assumptions and conclusions that were never drawn.

In all their lives, Marcus and Janet were each essentially one person, each lifetime being the equivalent of a different experience, shaping the ultimate determination or outcome of the next experience. It was presumably a learning process, and Janet was obviously a hard learner, having difficulty working herself out of the cheerless, menial pattern.

There was also no attempt to point out that she might have to pay sometime in the same coin for taking her own life. For I was no believer then in reincarnation's law of karma, which made suicide, karmically, a violation of the life process which would have to be learned one day.

Melina was too intangible, too subjective, too sketchy and remote for proof. But she also spoke of Egypta and Atlantis, and of Incan culture and lore, and no attempt was made to weave this together with the legendary story of a Lost Continent destroyed in a holocaust, and band of straggling survivors dispersing to Egypt, Peru, and Mexico, founding cultures superior to anything the native population could have generated of themselves.

The effort to relate her remarkable memory to her writing was not made until she slipped back into the Athens of the dictator Pericles, the courtesan Aspasia, and Hippocrates, the father of medicine. She was Helena then, a student of medicine, with the help of Horetius, then an instructor. She pictured unique treatments and surgery with such detail that I was inevitably reminded of *Dear and Glorious Physician.* Graphically, she described the probing surgery for a malignancy on the brain. "You will notice it is an evil color. It is not the faint pink of the normal brain; it is like a giant spider with tentacles. Some doctors call it the Crab. Each of those tentacles must be removed, or they will grow again."

I did not make enough of the symbology she used. For the Crab was the symbol of the astrological sign of Cancer, and no doctor of ancient or medieval times, including Hippocrates, practiced medicine without some help from astrology.

There was more, much more, about the body and its ills,

the Sweet Sickness, which was diabetes, and the White Sickness, which was tuberculosis. I had always thought Jenner was the first to inoculate for smallpox, but it was old hat to the Egyptians—her Egyptians. And there was more about cancer, suggesting that some forms of this malignancy were passed down in families. "If a mother has a tumor in the breast, her daughters will very likely get it. It could be hereditary, but it could also be from the mother's milk. We have proved that cancer is contagious. If it is cancer of the lungs, wear a mask over your face and do not touch any part of the exudate."

After this session she sat up on the couch, dangling her legs and smoking a cigarette, her eyes half-closed in rapt concentration. The idea of a book on this subject was stirring in the deepest recesses of her mind. But, ironically, she didn't know why, for she had no conscious recall of what she said and still no input from us. She knew little consciously about Hippocrates, little more about Pericles and Aspasia, and the names Horetius and Helena meant nothing to her.

"When did you first think of such a book?" I asked.

"I'm not sure. But it seems to have been building for a while."

"What would it deal with?"

"I suppose Pericles and Aspasia's love life together. Pericles was quite a figure and is responsible for Athens being the beautiful city it is today. And Aspasia was the most beautiful and resourceful woman in Athens."

She caught herself for a moment and looked puzzled. "I don't know why I should know all this."

"Had you thought about it before coming out?"

"Oh, I had some thoughts of it, but nothing compulsive."

If any age moved Janet, it was the time Christ trod the earth on his tragic path to immortality. And as I thought of Him on the Cross I remembered His saying, "Follow me," and felt now this must have been what He was thinking when He asked His disciples to abandon all else and walk with Him.

Readers continually asked when she was to write the

definitive story of the Master. But she would only murmur, "Sometime . . . later."

She had written emotionally of Christ in *Dear and Glorious Physician, Great Lion of God,* and *Dialogues with the Devil.* And her narratives often conflicted with what we knew of the past. Paul's Jewish family casually spoke of reincarnation, which neither Christianity nor orthodox Judaism accepted. She painted vivid pictures of Peter and Paul, Luke and John and James, and the other Apostles, though, curiously, there was no explicit picture of Christ. He was seen obliquely, in the distance, like the sun that could not be stared into because of its overwhelming radiance.

Somewhere in her subconscious lurked strange and wondrous tales of that hallowed age and the unforgettable martyrs who changed the world. And so I was not surprised during one session when, in a halting voice, she spoke of the sacred hills of Galilee and a daughter, then fourteen, Miriam of Magdala. The Anglicized Miriam was of course Mary—Mary of Magdala, Mary Magdalene. I listened with a twinge of expectation. She was a simple housewife, Hannah bat Jacob, the wife of Ephraim, ordinary country folk, neighbors, had they known it, of one Yeshua ben Joseph of Nazareth.

We heard that all over Israel people were praying and dreaming of the Messiah who would one day soon liberate the Jews from the stern Roman yoke. In a dream Hannah saw not the sad-faced, olive-skinned Jesus of the Renaissance painters, but a tall, sinewy youth with a direct blue gaze and flowing hair of reddish gold. She rejoiced as she saw this Deliverer of Israel, promised by the prophet Isaiah, holding her beloved daughter in His arms. How great a day that would be!

I was so caught up in the story that I no longer thought of the woman stirring on the couch as Taylor Caldwell. Still as the mother of the Magdalene, she was now combing the Jerusalem streets for the daughter who had run away years before, rather than traditionally marry a man with an affliction similar to hers—a yetzer-hara, a cast in one eye. Hannah's steps took her to the city square, where Yeshua was standing up to a crowd stoning a young woman. She did not recognize this woman at first. Then, as she pushed through the crowd, she saw with a gasp that it was her longlost daughter. She let out an unearthly wail. "They are killing my daughter," she cried, "they are killing my daughter." Again and again she repeated the cry, sobbing, "They are stoning her to death! God help her!"

The man she now recognized as the blue-eyed, golden-maned man of her dream bent low to the pavement and thrust His body between the stone throwers and their victim. Then He boldly raised His eyes and said in a voice that cracked like a whip through the square: "Let him who has not lain with this woman, let him throw the first stone."

The throng drew off, muttering, and we were jarred back to reality as the woman on the couch bolted upright, wringing her hands and moaning. "Is something wrong with one of my daughters? Is something wrong with Judy?"

We tried to reassure her, and yet were so affected by her emotion that we put off the sessions for the day. After a couple of cigarettes she seemed composed, though her brow still knotted as if trying to piece a puzzle together.

I was familiar, as was nearly everyone, with the rebuke Jesus had given the mob stoning the Magdalene for adultery. And like Jan Robinson, I was struck by the discrepancy in Janet's quotation.

I turned curiously to Janet, who was now stroking her temples as though to rub away any lingering confusion.

"Can you answer a question?" I asked.

She nodded silently.

"Do you recall Christ's remarks to the mob stoning the fallen woman?"

Her face wrinkled in distaste. "Of course I do, those hypocrites. Jesus said, 'He that is without sin among you, let him cast his first stone at her.'"

There was a significant difference. And we all agreed that it was most likely that an aroused Christ would have gone directly to the attack. He was not one to mince words.

Chapter Ten

POINT, COUNTERPOINT

JANET was in a mood to kick up her heels. "After all," she said, with an owlish grin, "Grandma was going strong at the century mark."

She turned to Jan Robinson. "Why don't you get Harold Robbins on the phone, and we'll discuss that movie he wants to do?"

"He's interested in *Dynasty of Death*," said Jan. "You don't want to let that go for a song."

I wondered how a novelist, even one as popular as Harold Robbins, could make a motion picture out of one of her books when the studios hadn't been able to.

"They could have," Jane said. "They kept buying my books, then got scared off by the expense of filming these whoppers."

One studio had bought *This Side of Innocence*, then shelved it. Another took *Dear and Glorious Physician*, but shied off after splurging millions on Elizabeth Taylor's *Cleopatra*. Walter Wanger, the producer, had acquired the motion picture rights to *Dynasty*, and Janet had bought them back from the Wanger estate.

"Robbins is quite a writer," she said. "He should be able to do a screenplay."

Jan made a phone call and said that the novelist had suggested dinner at a fashionable Hollywood restaurant, with his agent, Jan, and myself, if I cared to join them.

"Good," said Janet, "I'm tired of lying on a couch, wondering what the hell I'm talking about."

The dinner was apparently a productive one. The food was excellent, the wine superb, and the service incomparable. Janet was charmed and impressed, despite her worldliness, by the deference shown her host.

"You mean," she said, "that the same table is reserved for you every night?"

He nodded carelessly.

And so the two took stock of each other, the country's best-selling male author and the best-selling female counterpart. They apparently liked what they saw. Jan had been prepared to see some large figures flung around by these two multimillionaires. But she had not counted on Janet's impulsive burst of generosity.

"Harold," she said, "you can option *Dynasty* for two thousand dollars." And then before the startled Jan could frame a protest, she added, with a wave of her hand, "And I'll throw in the two sequels, *The Eagles Gather* and *Time No Longer.* They're all the same book anyway."

Dynasty, the first of a trilogy about the Bouchard clan, had been so long originally that editor Maxwell Perkins had drawn off the last part of the manuscript and made two additional novels out of it, with some extra patchwork on Janet's part, of course.

Author Robbins demurred.

"Oh, no, I can't let you do that," he said, as Janet's business agent breathed a little easier for a moment.

And then Robbins showed how generous he could be.

"I'll give you fifty dollars for the rights to each additional book."

"All right," Janet agreed, as Jan went into shock. "It's a deal."

Actually, she was not all that charitable, for if the films were made and became money-makers, Janet would share in the profits.

"There won't be any profits," Jan Robinson said glumly later, calling on me to help change Janet's mind. It was like knocking on a steel door.

"I have all the money I need," said Janet, "I would like one of my books finally made into a movie, instead of everybody just talking about it."

Jan grimaced. "All I heard was talk, and you know what that's worth."

Janet's desire for a movie was amusing, since she never watched any. It had something to do, Jan explained, with her feeling of her own value. Hemingway, Steinbeck, John O'Hara, Pearl Buck—all had seen movies done of their major works. Even James Michener, whom Janet did not consider of the first rank.

"She would like to see one film," said Jan Robinson, "even if she was the only person in the audience."

But the Robbins affair was soon put on a back burner. Now that the sessions were nearly over, Janet wanted to know what she had said.

"Was it that awful?" she demanded. "Did I confess to murder?"

I still didn't want anything to influence her course of behavior.

"What behavior?" she snorted.

"How you live, and what you write."

She looked at me incredulously.

"Outside of Paddy," she said, "there is absolutely nobody in my life, and you know how those Irishmen are."

I wasn't having any more of the mythical Paddy.

"You have much to write, including the book on Jesus that everybody expects from you."

She threw up her hands. "After *Captains and the Kings* comes out, that's it. I've had it."

Jan put in helpfully, "How about the Crusades book Lee Barker suggested on Saladin and King Richard? That might be timely, with the Arab oil squeeze and all."

She shook her head. "I'm not bogging myself down in research. I have no ideas now except for Pericles and Aspasia."

In one of her forewords she had generously given Marcus

credit for helping her research the book and assist with the writing.

"I suppose you miss Marcus's helping hand," I said.

She snorted. "That was done to keep him busy. Can you imagine Marcus doing my writing.

Not a day passed that she didn't make some psychic prediction, either about Jan or myself, or whoever happened to drop by.

This day was no different.

"You're going to do another book with me," she said. "Do you know that?"

She turned to Jan. "You mentioned that old manuscript on Atlantis I did as a child. Why not, as you say, let him rewrite it and get it published?"

Jan had already shown me the massive manuscript. It presented a fascinating picture of a Lost Continent, decadent and depraved, held uncertainly together by a beautiful young Empress trying to withstand the challenge of a conquering Emperor from the North. There was also a romance, for the Empress stood in danger of not only losing her Empire to this rugged invader, but her heart as well. A bit hackneyed, perhaps, but still possessing some ingenious detail. There were obvious faults which had kept it from being published. Structurally, it was confusing and reflected the inexperience of a twelve-year-old. It required a clearer storyline and a little more plausibility.

She looked at me closely. "I would like you to do it," she said. "It may get you thinking."

"Why not rework it yourself, as you did *Dear and Glorious Physician*?"

"I don't have the patience. Besides, I have my reasons for you finishing it up."

"To make another prediction come true?"

She turned back to Jan. "Make sure he gets the manuscript."

"And who shall publish it?"

"Anybody you say; it shall be your book, and we'll share

whatever it brings."

She was champing to get away on her three-month world cruise on the Dutch luxury liner *Rotterdam.*

"When will I know what I've been gabbing about?" she demanded. "I suppose that I've been Cleopatra and the Queen of Sheba and everybody else glamorous and wonderful."

She caught Jan Robinson's amused glance.

"Now what are you two keeping from me?"

I couldn't resist. "I know now why you're always cold, hungry, and barefoot, and so desperately poor to begin with."

Her face perked up. "You mean I was some poor thing. Well, maybe there's some truth in it, then. Because I was certainly born a poor thing, unwanted by my parents. And it's never gotten any better. Even Marcus wound up with half my money, though we politely called it a Foundation."

The whole project had been a fascinating adventure, an excursion into time and a truly unique mind. But there were still some loose threads.

"Do you have any feeling about Marcus still being alive, hovering about, waiting somewhere to rejoin you at the proper time?"

She shook her head. "I can't see Marcus in somebody else's body. And if he were, he wouldn't be Marcus, would he?"

Obviously, nothing of what she had said about Estanbul—and Marcus—had slipped into her conscious mind.

She looked to Jan for support, and Jan nodded amiably. "I must admit," she said, "that it would be hard to find another Marcus."

It was apparent, nevertheless, that something of Marcus's steel-like determination had made her feel that if anybody could come back it would be Marcus. "He's a Taurus," she said with a smile, "and you know how stubborn they are."

In the quest for corroboration, I had the idea of having psychics read for Janet to see whether they would pick out something she had already dredged up. This, I thought, might validate the regressions somewhat, however unscientific it might seem to those making a science of researching the Unknown.

She protested feebly as I carted her off to the Reverend Douglas Johnson, a Hollywood psychic whose work I had described in *The Miracle Workers.*

"I had to bring her in," I explained to Johnson, "because the poor woman keeps talking about how she has written her last book and is not going to do anything now except enjoy herself."

Janet correctly read my lips and trumpeted, "Don't 'poor woman' me, and what's wrong with some fun before I die, which I may do at any moment."

Johnson laughed. "There's not much chance of that," he said. "I see you living a long life, and a productive one. You've got five or six more books in you. And I see your fame spreading."

She looked at him skeptically.

"What is it when you see brilliant black dots and white lights darting all over the place like mad?"

He gazed back solemnly.

"It could be a dark force building up, a restless spirit imprisoned by its own suicide."

Janet shook her head incredulously.

"It could be liver spots, you know."

"You will be surprised how much you will enjoy yourself on your world cruise."

She bristled disdainfully. "I suppose I'll meet a tall, dark, handsome man and marry him."

Johnson had a helpful sense of humor.

"Not anybody of that description," he smiled, "but you will marry. In fact, you will marry twice."

Janet made an exclamation of disgust.

"At least," she said, "the spirits don't think I'm over the hill."

We were at the door, about to leave, when Johnson gave us a curious look. "You two knew each other before," he said in obvious surprise.

As she snorted, he smiled again in his assured way. "And you will do much together."

Outside, she was still shaking her head. "Married twice over at my age. Isn't that shameful?"

But her eyes sparkled mischievously.

Something else he said had struck me, reviving some of my earlier speculation.

"Do you really feel you knew me before?"

She threw it off with a laugh. "Oh, that, what would he know?"

After some prompting, Janet finally agreed to see another psychic, the English-born medium, the Reverend George Daisley, who had gained prominence as Bishop Pike's channel to the "other side."

"It may be nice," she said, "to see somebody else in a trance for a change."

Nevertheless, she grumbled all the way to Santa Barbara, constantly asking whether we were driving to Alaska, when actually the trip was but ninety miles or so. By the time the car rolled up to Daisley's rambling ranchhouse, she was in a vexatious mood.

As Daisley came forward to greet us, I took one look at her and whispered, "Give him a chance."

Janet still complained about the California cold, even with the temperature in the seventies, and wore a borrowed woolen pants suit, which had become her uniform. As Daisley led us to a small studio, back of the house, she shivered in the noonday sun.

Inside, as we sat around in a small circle, Janet lit up a cigarette. Daisley frowned.

"You will have to put out your cigarette, Madam. This is a very special room."

Janet glared but snuffed out the cigarette. She gave him a tight smile, apparently having made up her mind that she didn't like this disagreeable man.

Closing his eyes, the pleasant-faced, graying medium fluttered his hands and announced casually that the spirits were present in great numbers.

"I get a name like Mark," he said. "Your husband is standing just to the left of you, and I'm to tell you that he is placing a red rose near you."

Janet snorted in disbelief. "Marcus never bought a flower in his life. And nobody ever called him Mark."

"Marcus" tried valiantly to convince her of his presence, mentioning trips together to Venice and St. Mark's Square, to Majorca, and the Chopin house, where the consumptive composer had lived with French novelist George Sand.

Janet sniffed outrageously.

"Is that all he has to say?"

Daisley's face became a little strained.

"Your husband is very close. He always thought that when somebody died that was the end. Now he knows better." He held his head up high and appeared to be listening. "He's saying, 'I told Janet if there was any truth to an afterlife, I would let her know. That is why I am manifesting myself.'"

Janet shook her head and Daisley struggled on.

"I am to remind you how you stood together with your husband at Chopin's piano and discussed his romance with the French writer."

She was adamant. "I don't remember."

Daisley's voice became vehement.

"Marcus says, 'For God's sake, tell her I am still alive. Tell her to go on because her work isn't done yet. Her greatest success is yet to come.'"

Janet laughed out loud, and Daisley flushed to the roots of his hair.

"He has gone off now," he said, struggling to retain his composure, "but he says you will remember before the day is over."

Despite certain reservations about trance mediums, I was impressed and could see that Jan Robinson was similarly affected. But there was no budging Janet.

"Who is Mary Ann?" Daisley suddenly asked. "She

wants to say hello."

"I don't know any Mary Ann," Janet said shortly.

"Mary Ann Evans," Daisley elaborated, as Jan Robinson and I exchanged glances at this unexpected reference to George Eliot.

Daisley continued eagerly. "Mary Ann is saying, 'I want you to know I have been inspiring your writing, and there are times when I have helped you over difficult passages.'"

Was this, if true, in expiation for having allowed her little scullery maid to be thrown wrongly into prison, then forsaking her so that she took her own life?

Janet, of course, had no recollection of what she had said under hypnosis.

"Who is this Mary Ann?" she insisted.

Jan Robinson said impatiently, "Mary Ann Evans—George Eliot, whose writings you were familiar with as a child."

There was more from the author of *The Mill on the Floss*.

"After your suicide, she learned you were unjustly accused, and she mourned your death."

"It's all a mystery to me," said Janet with a shrug of her shoulders. "I just don't believe in all this nonsense."

Daisley heaved a big sigh. He had been on the receiving end for two hours and was ready to call it a day.

"Your husband says you will believe one day."

On the way back everyone appeared strangely thoughtful. We stopped off for dinner, and Janet insisted on treating as usual, repeating her customary, "You're deductible."

She knew that she had not behaved well.

"You know," she said, sipping slowly on her bourbon, "something that man said stirred some hidden chord of memory."

"And what was that?" I asked stiffly, still put off by her behavior.

"That scene in Majorca. I remember now that we did go into Chopin's house together, where he lived with George Sand [Baroness Dudevant]. I remember standing at the piano and looking around the bleak house and saying to Marcus, 'This is definitely no place to recover from tuberculosis.'"

Thus encouraged, I asked, "Have you felt at any other time that Marcus was trying to communicate?"

She looked over at Jan, and I could see they shared a secret which she finally decided to let me in on.

"On the day Marcus expired, I called the hospital and they said he was in a terminal coma, dead for all practical purposes, but with traces of vital signs that presupposed life. I was waiting for Jan to pick me up. We were planning to have early dinner, then go on to the hospital."

It was just before six, and she was alone in the living-room except for the dog, Robert, her beloved boxer. She thought she heard a rustle in the room, and she could see the dog bristle a little, nervously flick out his tongue, then look toward the balcony and let out a mournful wail.

As he howled again, still staring up at the balcony, she put her hand to her forehead and gasped. "For the twinkling of an eye, I thought I saw Marcus at the head of the staircase in the suit he had expressed a wish to be buried in. He smiled behind his eyeglasses and waved as if saying good-bye."

At that moment Jan Robinson walked in and the phone rang. Seeing Janet distracted, she picked it up and listened for a moment, her face growing somber. She hung up and turned to Janet with a sympathetic look. "That was the hospital," she said. "Marcus died just moments ago."

There were now tears in Janet's eyes. "Later, he spoke to me in my dreams, and one time he stood by my bed, shaking his head over my tears. He told me to get on with life, not to wish for death. And he—Estanbul—would be waiting when I got there.

Chapter Eleven

TAYLOR LIVES AGAIN

THE ocean-going *Rotterdam*, average passenger age seventy-plus, touched off at San Francisco near the end of the world cruise, and I flew up with Jan Robinson to greet the voyaging author. I didn't know what to expect, though given a clue in a radiogram sent from the ship:

"Miriam Taylor Holland Caldwell Combs Reback is going to take time off for herself. (Well, for a couple of hours a day, anyway.) I always had someone to take care of. Now I am going to do something for me. I went to the ship's dentist today and had my teeth cleaned—without the general anesthetic I usually demand—and get. Also, I am going to have an old ingrown tooth removed. I also bought some perfume today and some lipstick and eye shadow. (Too late?) Also some silk nightgowns and pants. My daughter Peggy, who is traveling with me, doesn't know what to make of all this. I am also taking up yoga on the ship and was congratulated on my muscle tone and limberness."

I had passed the note to Jan, who observed drily:

"Sounds to me like a man."

We boarded the ship with high expectations. Within a few minutes a vivacious Taylor Caldwell descended on us and, chattering gaily, as if she had seen us but the day before, led us directly to her stateroom. I marveled how sprightly she was, how confident, as the words tumbled out. Jan looked around inquiringly for Peggy, but she was nowhere to be seen.

"Probably at lunch," she decided.

There was a new sparkle in Janet's eye, a new lilt to her

voice. She was magnificent in a flowing dress which showed off a dazzling new necklace of diamonds and rubies.

"Everett bought it for me in Bombay." she said with bright enthusiasm. "He's such a dear."

Jan raised an inquiring eyebrow.

Janet rushed on breathlessly.

"Oh, you don't know, of course. It's a sort of engagement present. He proposed and I accepted. We are planning to be married. Maybe."

The manuscript under my arm seemed almost an intrusion. But she was too happy to be anything but helpful.

"The ship is stopping over for two or three hours," she said, "we can have lunch, take a look at the manuscript, and you can meet Everett."

Everett came as rather a surprise. He was nothing like the lordly, if ephemeral, Paddy. He was short and squat, with a square face, short neck, and bullish shoulders. He reminded me of Marcus. They seemed out of the same mold. Everett was seventy-eight and looked it. His face was a dead gray under his tan.

"He has been married seven times," Janet announced proudly. "He's quite a catch. All the ladies on the boat were chasing after him."

Everett was in real estate, commerce, and sundry other business ventures, vaguely dismissed with an airy wave of her hand. "He is enormously successful," she said.

Everett remained coolly detached, his gimlet eyes wandering from Jan Robinson to myself as if sensing a possible problem.

She turned to him affectionately. "Jan, as I told you, is my business manager, and this man"—she nodded cheerfully in my direction—"is my longtime friend and colleague. I told you of the book in which I supposedly said so many amazing things I know nothing about."

Everett's ears pricked up. "I would like to see it," he said crisply, "and make sure it doesn't hurt Janet. You know, she has her reputation to consider."

I gave him a second look and smiled to myself. It was almost as if Marcus was back.

Jan Robinson's eyes caught mine, and I could see the same thought in her mind.

Everett held out his hand, but I made no move to turn over the manuscript to him. There was an awkward silence, and we all sat looking at each other until Jan Robinson tactfully changed the subject.

"Where is Peggy?" she asked, peering out the stateroom door.

"She's gone," said Janet with a chuckle. "The poor girl is so proper. She said I was the scandal of the boat. And so she got off at the last port and took herself home."

Everett had Marcus's singlemindedness. He was frowning now, the lines puckering between his eyebrows.

"I would like to see the manuscript," he repeated, extending his hand.

Janet's eyes ran over my face, read it correctly, then turned to her bridegroom-to-be.

"What for?" she said brusquely. "It has nothing to do with you. My writing is a private part of my life. That's what I tried telling Marcus."

Everett's face dropped. I felt a certain sympathy for him, since I was sure she had encouraged the belief that he would be handling her affairs.

As he looked on a little bewildered, Janet glanced curiously at the manuscript, which made a rather formidable pile.

"I'll read it on the ship." She smiled in atonement at Everett, who was sulking a little. "That will give me something to do. And I'm sure it will do no harm if Everett glances through it. He's such a dear."

There were first a few things I wanted to go over with her.

"What," I asked, "is a *yetzer-hara?*"

She frowned. "What do I know about a yetzer-hara? I never heard anything like that before."

Jan Robinson put in helpfully, "You talked about a

yetzer-hara while you were under hypnosis, in a past life.''

She trumpeted disdainfully. "How could that be? I never had a past life.''

Everett looked at us as if we had all gone mad.

"What's the difference between a synagogue and a temple?'' I asked.

Her expression was a perfect reflection of Everett's.

"There is no difference, everybody knows that. Both are places of worship.''

"You pointed out a difference, at least in Biblical times.''

She seemed even more bewildered.

"The synagogue was a place of worship at that time,'' offered Jan, on the basis of some hasty research, "but it was also a community center, for social groups as well as prayer groups. The temple was exclusively a house of worship.''

I had another surprise for her.

"You mentioned so many old Hebrew words that Jan went to an expert at UCLA [University of California at Los Angeles] to find out what they mean. Yetzer-hara, which was one of them, means the bad side or evil spirit of something. You had a daughter with a cast to her eye, and that was a yetzer-hara.''

"I have two daughters,'' she said staunchly, "and neither has a cast in her eye.''

"This was in a past life, and your daughter''—I could not resist—"was Mary Magdalene.''

Janet's jaw dropped. "What did you do to me?'' she demanded.

Everett was immediately protective. "I don't think it's proper to speak to Janet this way,'' he said.

"It's nothing to be taken seriously.'' She shook her head impatiently, then quickly patted Everett's hand. "Nobody has been so kind to me in years,'' she said, giving him a radiant look.

Whatever it was, it agreed with her. Her face was rosy-hued, her eyes bright; she moved with the agility of a young woman. She positively glowed.

"You know," she said, her eyes snapping, "my mind has been filled with bright images of ancient Greece. I see all sorts of shadowy figures moving through the Acropolis and the councils of government, and beautiful courtesans consoling the harried heads of state in luxurious baths."

"You've got your Pericles book," I said, "thanks to the couch."

I handed her the manuscript. "Remember, please—your epilogue."

As we got up to leave, I congratulated them both and wished Everett luck.

Janet chuckled.

"He's going to need it. He's a Pisces man, and you know how dolorous they can be. They're such martyrs, and so moody, not like Taureans, who you can stoke food into and keep happy."

She regarded him possessively.

"The poor dear was so jealous when I mentioned that Paddy also proposed." I saw Everett's face tighten at Paddy's name.

She turned to me with a smile. "You know how charming Paddy is. You met him at a party in New York."

I said, merely to see how she reacted, "I think it was on the ship."

She had no trouble reading my lips. She started a little and gave me a searching look. She opened her mouth to speak, then changed her mind.

"Oh, yes," I said, "I remember him well."

A small smile played on her lips, and her eyes looked challengingly into mine. She had not fooled me, but I did not fool her.

She started to leaf idly through the manuscript, nodding approvingly as she skipped through some of the regressions. "I'm glad I was never a man," she said. "I was a liberated woman long before Women's Lib."

I pointed out that she had never repeated a time period. The nearest thing to an overlapping life came when, as poor

Wilma, she died prematurely in England in 1898.

Janet continued to flip through the pages. Suddenly her eyes stopped. She had come to the part where a gifted life reader of past life experiences, the late Violet Gilbert, had without ever having met Janet touched on her past lives in Atlantis and in the Biblical period.

"As a writer, you have been a pioneer, a builder who chose to serve in this manner. And that goes back to the time Christ walked the earth. Yes, you were there."

Janet's eye stopped at this line.

"How would that woman know all this?"

"The same way," I said, "that you knew about Darios and Lucifer and Melina."

I could see Everett's eyes boggle, and he looked around the table as if he was in an asylum. But the most amazing passage was to come.

"And when you knew that the birth of the Messiah had occurred, you continued to prepare, praying for this opportunity to see what you had been preparing for and make the way ready. You were still in body when He began His ministry. But you had only asked to live long enough to see His mission placed into motion. You had not asked to see it completed. And so it was at this time your spirit left the body."

And so it had in the regression, Hannah bat Jacob dying from the shock of her encounter with her long-lost daughter, after kissing the feet of the Master.

A fascinated Janet shook her head at what she had read.

"I can't believe it. Are you sure you didn't make it up?"

She put the manuscript under her arm and stood up with Everett lacing her arm through his. The warning bell had sounded for our departure.

"I'll have my reading done by the time you finish your book, and the epilogue will be with it." She gave me a roguish look. "And I'll let you know more about what happens on the good old *Rotterdam*."

On her return her publisher was throwing a party to launch *Captains and the Kings*, and she insisted I be there for the introduction of Everett to her literary world. Her eyes moved down Everett's unprepossessing frame. "You wouldn't think to look at him," she said, "that he's had more wives than Henry the Eighth."

Everett winced the least bit. He might as well get used to it, I thought.

I heard from her soon after she got home. It was a meaty letter full of gossip about her affair of the heart. I could well believe that she had not had as much fun in thirty years. She referred endearingly to Everett as the Boyfriend, and knowing Marcus's moroseness, I sympathized.

"After we left San Francisco," she wrote, "the Boyfriend moved into the stateroom with me, but kept his own in which to sulk after I developed some reservations about marrying in haste. A number of gentlemen called to invite me to cocktails, saying, 'Now that your chaperone daughter has gone, would you have a drink with me?' The Boyfriend would angrily answer the phone before I could get to it and say, 'Mrs. Reback does not accept dates with STRANGE men.' I wonder who he thought he was. The steward was all discretion and would lower his eyes on bringing us breakfast and would courteously pretend that it was Peggy in the other bed. NOT THAT THERE WAS ANYTHING GOING ON, OF COURSE!

"The whole ship became involved in the ROMANCE. Three people from Buffalo snubbed me after the Romance began, but everyone else was elated and full of gossip. I can't understand why. Though Peggy accused me of 'indiscretion,' I was most discreet. It was true that before she went off I would leave the Boyfriend's stateroom at 4:00 or 5:00 A.M., after LONG TALKS, and would be escorted back to my stateroom by the night watchman, who exchanged polite remarks to me. But that was all. Of course the Captain got involved. He told Peggy, 'I can't put the gentleman off the ship. Your mother is not complaining about him!'

"It is very hilarious, and I will tell you about it all when we sit down privately. But, sad to say, between Peggy and the Boyfriend they kept me VIRTUOUS (maybe). And I've had enough of that to last a lifetime. Marcus was all business and thought of me as a writing machine. And it's hard for my daughters to think of me as needing some man to love.

"When Peggy dear got upset with me, she cried out, 'Remember this: You belong to your daughters and not to any goddam man!' As the stateroom door was open at that time, my neighbors were edified. It is most humorous, and when I think of all the episodes which took place I burst out laughing—and believe me, I haven't laughed so much in eons. In fact, I had more joy and fun and excitement and love in three months of the cruise than in the previous three decades, which were very dreary ones, indeed."

She had a lingering fear that marriage might ruin a beautiful friendship. Everett, now concerning himself with Janet's spiritual well-being, after seven marriages of his own had implausibly proposed a Church wedding.

"The Boyfriend, who insists he is not Catholic, forced me to make my Easter Duty, and called Monsignor to hear my confession on Good Friday, and then had a talk with Monsignor which lasted for two hours. When he came back, looking depressed, I said, 'I hope you were discreet and didn't tell Monsignor all.' And he confessed he did, and I shrieked, 'For God's sake, then I am in a state of mortal sin, you idiot!' This led to sulks and a retreat to his own stateroom and my acceptance of a cocktail date from another gentleman, and the Boyfriend, who must have ESP, roared into the stateroom and said, 'I know you have been up to something! Get dressed and come to the bar with me.' Being a Pisces, he SEES things, notably things I try to keep a secret from him. After we got back, I took him to see Marcus's and my tomb out in the cemetery, and he looked over the huge lot I have and said, nastily, 'Are you thinking of starting a housing development here for all your husbands?' I thought that most unkind of him. After all, I have had only two, not seven, which he has had."

I could only marvel at her. At seventy-three or so, she showed more zest and life than most people at thirty. And her

interests were universal, for she was as concerned with the
regressions she had now gone over as with a new love. They
seemed to trigger a memory mechanism never far from the surface. And as a writer, she was doubly involved, analyzing these
subconscious recalls as she would a novel.

"It would seem that with one or two exceptions I was a
person in very humble circumstances, an abused little slavey, a
scullery maid, a desperate and starving young woman who
died in neglect, and other sad conditions. If so, then that ex-
plains my concern, since childhood, for the afflicted and the
hopeless and the suffering, and for my present charities and
scholarships. Apparently no one ever helped me—as no one
did in my present life—but I have anonymously helped
thousands."

Just as she had experienced a backswell of memory about
ancient Greece and Pericles and Aspasia, she now had a new
flow of recollections after reading about poor Jeannie McGill.

"A curious thing has happened to me since I 'divulged'
that I was a scullery maid at the age of about thirteen to Mary
Ann Evans [George Eliot]. I can 'see' her house in London
with a clarity which sometimes horrifies me. I was never, in
this life, in her house. Yet I know all the rooms, the dark staircase with paneled-oak wall, the narrowness of it, the long up-
per corridor from which the rooms opened, the coal fireplaces
of dark marble, and I can 'feel' the very texture of carpets
under my feet, smell the coal gas, the odors of the big, dim,
bricked kitchen, and the feel of damask under my fingers on
the wall, in a tone of deep crimson. I can see the narrow, wet
garden and 'remember' the gleaming yellow daffodils in the
Spring. I can 'remember' how cold I always was, cold to my
very bones. (I still hate cold.) I see the spit in the kitchen
fireplace and can smell the dripping fat of lamb and pork and
beef, and 'remember' how I would huddle close for warmth
and would sometimes steal a hot morsel as it slowly turned. I
could draw a picture of that tall, thin, gloomy house opening
on the wet street. I can still 'hear' the rattle of carriages on the
bricks, the clomp of horses, and see the smoke lying low on

chimney pots and flowing over slate roofs, and the black um-
brellas of scuttling pedestrians, and I 'remember' how
dolorous and abandoned I felt, how desolate and cold, and
how I hated the slow gray drip of the rain and the sound of the
wind against the windows. My novelist's imagination? Or
memory? I cannot say. I can only feel if there is a God, then
He was very harsh to me, and my brief 'life' in that incarnation
was pointless and certainly did not result in any benefit to me
as 'Karma' or 'enlightenment.'"

Was she the devil's advocate once more? I looked again
to make sure I had read her properly. "If there is a God"—this
from the author of *Dear and Glorious Physician* and *Great
Lion of God*. What had Lee Barker said about her being an
"agin-er," taking opposite and often conflicting sides to con-
fuse and demoralize the opposition?

She was truly one of a kind, as I was to note once again
when I saw her next, in her $300-a-day hotel suite in New York
before her publisher's party. She was excited about the
success of *Captains and the Kings*, which had immediately
jumped on the best-seller list and was due for a long stay.
Everett was very much in evidence, hovering about zealously.
He had become her business manager, knowing nothing about
the publishing business.

"Everett," she said fondly, "has found a new literary
agent for me."

"I thought Everett was in real estate," I said.

"Oh, he is very versatile. He owns properties in Jacksonville, and we intend to live there in a house Everett is having
built for me—that is," with an arch look for him, "if we get
married."

She looked quite regal in a lace dress with a sprinkling of
jewelry, and I would have thought of Cornelia again except for
a new softness which was obviously a tribute to love.

But her mood quickly changed, and her eyes snapped
angrily as she thought about the hometown reaction to her
romance. "The vicious remarks of my so-called 'friends' in
Buffalo that Everett is marrying me for my money are pure

malice. He could buy and sell me twice over, according to my banker in Jacksonville and my own lawyers.''

Everett shrugged and poured the coffee. He seemed mildly amused.

Janet abruptly stood up and gave herself a quick once-over in a mirror.

''Am I so unattractive that my friends must automatically assume that every man interested in me is after my money?''

Everett murmured a few soothing words. ''But you are a genius, my dear.''

She gave him a scathing look.

''No woman wants to be thought a genius by the man she loves.''

Everett's seven wives stood him in good stead.

''Yes, my dear,'' he said, waddling out of the room.

She heard, in her deafness, what she wanted to hear.

''Many people hinted that 'he was after your money,' though they didn't know a single thing about the poor lamb. I was outraged—as a woman—at the implication that I couldn't inspire affection in a man for myself alone, but only for my cash. I have had husbands who had no money at all, only ponderous debts when I married twice before. At least they loved me, even if I fell out of love somewhat rapidly later.''

In the meantime, a crisis had developed. She had told Everett she liked masterful men, and he had taken her at her word. Her voice reflected her incredulity. ''The gentleman is trying to cut down on my boozing and smoking and working at night, and isn't too fond of my religion, though he is a lapsed Catholic himself. I warned him not to interfere with the bourbon and the cigs and my faith, but he finds himself—he thinks—in a confident situation and so is putting the pressure on. I will have to put a stop to him. Not permanently, of course. I am too fond of him.''

So far there had been no mention of the epilogue.

''I preferred to discuss it privately,'' she said, reaching into a drawer and coming out with a handful of typewritten pages.

I began reading and saw at once that she had been strongly

affected by her experience. She again found satisfaction that she had always been female—never male.

"Some reincarnationists say there is no sex in the soul, that one can be born a man or a woman. This is particularly repulsive to me. I was glad to discover that I was never a man in previous 'lives.' I am glad I am a woman. I never had any desire to be a boy or a man in this present life. I am very fond of men, and I like my role as a woman with all the superior advantages which women have. And if there is reincarnation, I can only pray I will be born female again. And that men are still men in the world."

Into the epilogue went her misgivings and wonderment. "How explain my knowledge of ancient Hebrew and Spanish and Italian, languages I never knew? How explain my knowledge of ancient and modern medicine, which doctors have said is amazingly accurate? How explain my recitation of an intricate brain operation, which surgeons have said is meticulously true? I have never studied medicine, have never seen an operation, never had one myself, shudder at the sight of blood. Yet, I have written two medical novels at which eminent physicians have marveled for their accuracy."

I was impressed that she had found some evidence for reincarnation. But then, typically, she announced she had no explanation for the information that came through her.

"This is my disclaimer. I do not believe in reincarnation. I see no actual proof of it. I have thought that I have seen 'ghosts' on many occasions, and I have deluded myself that I have spoken to them. I do believe in ESP, but I believe it is a faculty of the human brain which will soon be revealed and used—an animal faculty humanity has almost lost (I converse with my dog through ESP). I do not believe it is an attribute of the 'soul,' for I am not convinced there is such a thing as the 'soul.' Nor is it occult or mysterious. It is an electric impulse of the brain, which perishes with all else at death."

As I put down the epilogue, she searched my face anxiously.

"You are disappointed after all your work?"

Curiously, she had made no reference to two compelling episodes—that of Fra Savanarola, in the medieval Florence she had recalled with a shudder, and again as the mother of the Magdalene, the most exciting episode in the book.

"Not really," I said, "for your honest opinion is what I wanted. And while you may not have become a believer, you have made a believer of me. And for that I am grateful. I could never quite accept reincarnation, but when you collapsed after seeing your daughter stoned in Jerusalem that day, I felt you must have been there to have seen your child raised from the dust by Christ, and reacted as you did. I have never witnessed such emotion as you manifested at that moment. Unfortunately, you could not see yourself."

It struck me as odd that she should remember what George Eliot's house was like, and the romance of Pericles and Aspasia, and not have some additional recall about a memory sufficiently powerful to precipitate her "past-life" death.

She shivered a little and said, with a faraway look, "As I read of Mary of Magdala, the whole terrible scene at the market place emerged, and I saw that poor girl's thin, tortured face and the helpless horror in her eyes. What mother wants to keep reliving all that?"

"This is not now, but two thousand years ago," I said. "It is what came off the tape."

She gave a troubled sigh. "I don't want to think about it." She turned away, exhausted.

At this point Everett returned to the room, carrying a scrap of paper for her signature.

She brushed a weary hand over her eyes. "Please take care of it, Everett," she said. "Whatever it is, it can't really matter."

Chapter Twelve

ATLANTIS

THE party was in full swing, and Janet, in this festive setting, reminded me of a resplendent Cornelia. She sat high in her chair, nodding, occasionally smiling, keeping herself the center of attention with just the proper touch of aloofness.

We sat on either side of Lee Barker, and he had been eagerly exploring her recent experience.

"After reading the most remarkable evidence for reincarnation," I said, "Janet said most emphatically that she saw no evidence for it. And if she doesn't believe in the continuity of life after her experience, I don't see why anybody else should."

Lee Barker pursed his lips judiciously.

"It's not all that bad," he said. "At least, it's an honest book."

"It would have been just as honest if she had drawn another conclusion."

He laughed pleasantly. "I told you she's an agin-er. That's why I won't let the publicity department put her on television. She'll be talking about *Great Lion of God* and say out of nowhere that she doesn't believe in God."

Janet looked at us a little impatiently.

"What are you two boys up to?"

"I'm just thinking," said Lee, "that you two should collaborate again."

Janet beamed.

"I had an idea for a play on shipboard. Everett gave it to me, inadvertently, of course. It is about an author who is presumably murdered on the ship and thrown overboard. Her husband, whom she has just married, becomes the major suspect. And then just when the gendarmes are about to haul hubby off in chains, the supposed victim turns up. She had been hiding out in the coal-bin, trying to throw suspicion on somebody she didn't like."

Her eyes gleamed dangerously.

"And then, while the ship's captain and his aides are trying to sort things out, she disappears into her cabin. When she doesn't come out, they investigate and find that her throat's been cut."

Thinking perhaps of *The Late Clara Beame*, Barker appeared less than enchanted.

"Who killed her and why?" he said.

She laughed triumphantly, showing her large Corneila-like teeth.

"That's for my collaborator to work out. I got him this far.

"Or," she went on gaily, "we could go a different route and do a comedy. Now I know nothing about playwriting, but it would be fun to bandy back and forth the actual dialogue with my daughter Peggy concerning my indiscretions. The whole situation was hilarious, and why couldn't the milieu be on ship? It would be so easy to stage. Some of the dialogue was damned lewd, too, and I am ashamed of myself. But that wouldn't hurt a play, not on Broadway. My own life could be shown in retrospect, hounded by priests and nuns and parents and husband and children, warned that I was born only to serve. With this for serious relief, the festivities with Everett on the ship become all the more comical."

"What would you call the play?" I asked.

She thought for a moment. "How about *Second Springtime for Mama*?"

Barker showed his goodhumored disapproval.

"Oh, don't be so solemn," she smiled. "It really doesn't

matter as long as there's four words in the title. That brings a book luck.''

She had proposed taking the "The" from our proposed title, *The Search for a Soul*, but was foiled by a conscientious copyeditor who thought its omission a mistake.

Barker, used to her little diversions, wasted no time on the play.

"The book I had in mind was a collaboration about Jesus." He spoke deliberately, moving his lips deliberately, so there would be no danger of her misunderstanding him.

"I have my own book on Jesus on the back burner," she said, "through the eyes of His sorrowing Mother."

"That sounds promising, but what about the book we discussed on Saladin and the Crusades?"

"Oh, that," she said, "I haven't tuned into that period. I'm going on with Pericles and Aspasia."

I turned to Barker. "What Jesus story did you have in mind?"

"Through the eyes of Judas, the most maligned man in history. What motivated the man? It couldn't have been the money; he threw that back. You could do the organizational work, and most of the writing, with Janet supplying the ideas and the finishing touches."

I had never written a book with anybody. The book we had just finished had been uncomplicated because our functions were so clearly divided.

"How do we go about it?"

"This is Janet's field. She would guide things, while you did the preliminary work and a first draft, which she could work over and change any way she wanted."

Janet's head bobbed forward.

"Curiously," she said, "I had the idea myself of a Judas book when finishing the last draft of *Dear and Glorious Physician*."

She had seen Judas as Christ's challenger, not His betrayer. Like other Judeans, he is searching for a militant Messiah who would free the Jews from the Roman yoke. But when Jesus shows no inclination to lead a military uprising, Judas forces Him to take a stand.

"To save himself," she went on enthusiastically, "Jesus must forgo His role as the Prince of Peace and take on the Roman legions. Even if He loses He is safe. What can the Romans do to this magician who heals the sick and blind, calms the errant seas, walks on water, and raises the dead? He even has the ability to disappear at will. Who would think that He would Himself choose to die on the cross?"

Before her eloquence, I felt a surge of excitement. What a book it would be, if it but conveyed what she felt.

I had just turned in one book on the psychic and was planning still another on the young Edgar Cayce, as a sequel to my *Sleeping Prophet*. It would be a relief to get into something else. But Janet was not quite ready. She wanted to do her novel on Mary first, and Pericles and Aspasia were already gestating.

"Meanwhile," she said, "we have *Atlantis* to collaborate on."

Barker's ears pricked up until told she had written the book when she was twelve and that several paperback houses had turned it down, even with her name. Jan Robinson had gone over the manuscript carefully. "There's just too much," she said, "and it's so disorganized. It needs more of a story line."

Janet gave her an incredulous look. "Now we have another publishing genius in the family."

Atlantis appealed to me. But I found *Judas* exciting.

"Why not have Judas tell the story, just as Matthew, Mark, Luke, and John told theirs?"

"You mean a sort of Fifth Gospel? Some people might find that blasphemous."

The conversation drifted off to other things, and I could see Everett just down the table anxiously craning his neck. He was seated next to a very charming lady, and I overheard her saying, during a lull in the conversation, "You know, Everett, Janet doesn't have as much money as you think."

His jaw dropped for a moment, but he rallied bravely. "I

don't care. It would just be a privilege to be her husband."

The dinner party finally drew to a close, with Janet smiling benignly at everybody.

"You are all invited to my wedding," she announced, with a regal smile and a flourish of her jeweled arms.

But when I saw her at her hotel the next day, she was again having second thoughts. Everett was adamant about living in Jacksonville, Florida, where he had married and lived before, and she still had her roots in Buffalo. "Everett," she confided, "gave me a deed to the new house where he wants us to live, if and when." Her voice fell and she looked cheerlessly around the empty hotel room. "I am still undecided. I asked if I could keep the jewelry he gave me—and the house—if we didn't marry. And he said no. I accused him of being an Indian-giver."

But she also had high praise for him which gave me an idea which way the wind was blowing. "He is one marvelous chef, not a cook but a talented chef. There is a difference, you know, as between the violinist in the pit and the one on the stage. Maybe he learned this from all the women he regularly married."

She sighed, and I caught the suspicion of moisture in her eyes.

"You know," she said, "I have always had the stupid idea since I was a baby that someone might truly love me sometime, but it never happened. And you can imagine what that has done to my self-esteem. Only the other day I acutely remembered a time when I was just three years old, in England, and my mother was talking to a neighbor and did not know I was in the next room. She said, 'You can beat her and kick her and almost scratch her eyes out, and pull out handfuls of her ugly red hair, and she will come crawling on her belly to you whimpering for affection.' Of course, she was speaking of me."

Her eyes had misted over by now.

"Am I so Gorgon-like in appearance, so repulsive of aspect, so despicable of character, so loathsome that I can never find anyone to honestly love me?"

At that precise moment, as if in response to her question, Everett came briskly into the room. He gave me a dark, lowering look, again reminding me of Marcus, and turned with businesslike crispness to Janet:

"You have to get rid of that Buffalo house. I'll offer it for sale."

I was about to leave when he stopped me with an unaccustomed smile. His voice was apologetic, almost ingratiating.

"By the way," he said, "can you describe this Paddy for me?"

Janet gave me a secret look.

I didn't hestitate. "Yes, of course. He is a handsome man, gifted, and rich. He owns homes all over the world and is madly in love with Janet."

Everett's face dropped, he grunted something unintelligible, and stiffly walked off.

It was the most gratifying lie I ever told.

At Janet's suggestion, I now signed the agreement making us equal partners of the new book, to be called *Romance of Atlantis.* We both assumed it would go to Lee Barker and Doubleday.

Meanwhile, the house in Buffalo went on the market and the wedding was on again. As the date approached, Jan Robinson showed a dwindling enthusiasm for the marriage. "With all that talk about his being a big tycoon," she said, "nobody knows anything about him."

"At least," I said, "he cared enough to buy her a new house and all that expensive jewelry."

Jan gave me an amused look.

"You must be kidding. She did all that."

Janet was still plotting the scenario to fit her image of her beau ideal.

I was hard at work on *Atlantis* when Janet was being married in Buffalo. I wired congratulations, hoping she would somehow find the love she needed. She had certainly had no luck with love in the past—any past.

Atlantis was truly formidable. How had a child had the patience to put so many words together, not knowing if her efforts would ever be rewarded? I read it through rapidly first and then slowly, hacking away at the extraneous verbiage. The style was florid and rather stilted, in the Victorian idiom of George Eliot. But some passages showed an intriguing wisdom, biting wit, disenchantment, and an alternating optimism and faith. Even when she wrote with a prophetic insight.

"Listen well to these words," the dying Emperor Lazar tells his daughter Salustra, "for they come as from beyond the grave. A ruler may make laws that are marvels of mechanical precision and justice, but he will still fail if he heeds not the hearts of those he rules. A fool loved by his subjects hath them always. A wise man unloved meets with stone ears. How thou wouldst ask did I keep the love of my people? Not by loving them, my daughter. This incontinent people, decadent in their sophistry, can only be ruled by knowing their vices, insolences, and ambitions. We have reached the heights of scientific achievement, but old moral standards, codes, and restraints have passed. The greater part of humanity is composed of greedy souls disguising their lust in family love, hiding their lascivious lips under pious smiles, loving their neighbors outwardly but hating them in their hearts.

"Take care, Salustra. Do not expect too much of these animals who, though they no longer swing by their tails, yet babble in the jargon of the jungle. Understand them, feed their vanity even more than their mouths, and they will love and acclaim thee."

Penetrating observations, these, from a twelve-year-old.

Atlantis was in trouble. The warlike Emperor Signar, from the rugged north country of Althrustri, had seized on the Emperor's death to invade his southern neighbor. Now, with the handsome Signar in control, an air of impending doom hung over the capital city. And Salustra, who had unhappily fallen in love with the hated conqueror, listens now to this lament as she plots the death of the man she loves:

Thou dost ask me why I weep, my maid.

Now hark while I tell thee why.
I weep for a corpse that is barely laid,
And the light in a vanished eye.
For lips I loved and no longer love;
For these do I groan and sigh.

Though no judge of poetry, the feeling in these few lines touched me.

I had tidied up the narrative, adding and subtracting, but essentially the bones were all there, barring a few minor adjustments. Salustra, in a jealous rage over Signar, slew her sister, Princess Tyrhia. I decided to kill off the fair Tyrhia in less fraternal fashion.

The destruction of Atlantis might very well have been the Biblical story of Noah, for the devastation began with a merciless downpour of forty days and nights. "Through the wide, deserted streets and canals of Lamora rushed the waters, swirling about the ancient statues and pillars, and carrying everything before them . . . the mountains seemed to dissolve into black rivers. The terrified people ran to higher ground, but the flood waters would not be denied. Meanwhile, the survivors blamed their Empress for their plight, not recognizing even then that their own wickedness had wrought their ruin."

Our adolescent author had undeniably produced an original with little reference to anything previously written. She had not so much borrowed from the Bible as she had, perhaps, tuned into the same source.

Even then she saw herself as she was to be—as the poised, aristocratic Cornelia, as the bejeweled, aloof Taylor Caldwell of her dreams. Was this from the distant past, or merely a psychic projection of the future?

The Atlantis book was assailed by captious critics who claimed her attacks on a decaying society were not those of a gifted child, but the contemporary prejudices of a well-known rightist author. "Why weren't we shown the original, untampered manuscript?" they wailed.

Nevertheless, the fact remained that sixty years earlier,

when she wrote of the lost continent off the North American shore, she had drawn striking social parallels to the America of the 1960s and 1970s long before she became a conservative, philosophically.

"Each year thousands of Althrustrians had seeped into the country, almost as an advance invasion force, lured by the wealth and comforts and opportunities of this favored land. Life was not hard and grim in Atlantis as it was in Althrustri, and laws here were more benign and tolerant. From other lands, too, the poorest classes of immigrants flowed into Atlantis, the adventurers, the paupers, the incompetent, the biologically inferior, having found existence too strenuous in their own country."

With all its ingenuity, I found revising *Atlantis* a tedious business. When I mentioned the difficulties, sympathizing with the editors who had rejected the original manuscript, Taylor was less than sympathetic.

"You especially should have no problem with it," she said.

When I failed to understand, she became impatient.

"Doesn't it stir anything in you?"

"Just a headache."

However, I did acknowledge finding myself intrigued by the undercurrents between Salustra and the Emperor Signar, hoping this fair flower of Atlantis would not do him in. From afar I kept making progress reports and sending queries, and she invariably gave me a satisfactory answer. And as with Pericles and Aspasia, she had considerable afterflow, apparently touched off by my observations, and as provocative as anything in the book.

"One night," she wrote, "dozing off, I suddenly found myself in the palace I wrote about in *Atlantis*, and I was Salustra. And guess who you were? And Jan Robinson was my younger sister. It was so clear and so vivid and imminent that when I woke up I could not orient myself for several minutes. I remembered every hall and room in the palace, and the colonnades, and the sea, and even a few words of the language! Imagine that. I felt that somewhere that palace and that country still existed, and I had only to find it, and I was filled for several hours with a sensation of despair and depression, in that it no longer existed—if it ever did. I distinctly remember saying to my sister, '*Zuhtah, canona pen utra*,' whatever the hell that means." (I never did find out.)

In *Atlantis* she projected herself as the Empress Salustra, fantasizing her romances and idealizing her throne. As Salustra, if this was she, she still knew no happiness, falling in love with a man loved by her sister, a man who had exploited a land that was her sacred heritage.

Even in this child book, she could not avoid the heroic power drive. It was inherent in nearly all her books, reflecting her own struggles, and was perhaps a commentary on her subconscious efforts to compensate for the ignominy of defeat and obscurity.

Her characters had this compulsive ambition from one book to the next. In *Captains and the Kings* the protagonist, Joseph Armagh, bears a striking resemblance to others with this singleminded obsession, Franz Stoessel, the ruthless steelmaker in *Strong City*, and the Bouchards in *Dynasty*. Like herself, they were poor and immigrants. Even the novels she extracted from history dealt with the Ghengis Khans, Caesars, and Richelieus (*Arm and the Darkness*), and Signar, of Althrustri and Atlantis, had the same power drive. But not all was moonlight and roses, for the game was not always worth the candle. During their greatest triumphs an uneasy pall hung over protagonists. They must pay for every moment of exaltation. There was no happiness without pain. The struggle for empire was fraught with pitfalls. We become aware of a higher power lurking capriciously in the wings, capable of demonstrating man's puniness at any moment. Even the title *Captains and the Kings*, from Kipling, was a reflection of the fleeting emptiness of empire:

> *The tumult and the shouting dies:*
> *The Captains and the Kings depart:*

> *Still stands Thine ancient sacrifice,*
> *An humble and a contrite heart.*

She now corresponded regularly from Jacksonville. Although she had little diversion in that Florida city, her marriage went along evenly for a while, and Janet seemed serenely happy. One thing troubled her—Everett's periodic absences, but she accepted this as a necessary business preoccupation until one day she was shockingly confronted with unmistakable evidence of Everett's infidelity.

I was shocked as well, but for a different reason. Seventy-nine?

She had, with feminine curiosity, opened a letter to Everett, and that had done it. There was no questioning the relationship it disclosed. Janet was furious. "I lay in wait for Everett to come back and jumped on him at once with lioness roars and charges. When, after an hour's recriminations and gallons of tears on my part, I had to pause from mere exhaustion, he said, 'You damned women make too much fuss about sex. What's a little romp in the hay, anyway?'

"I was almost—I say, almost—struck dumb at this monstrous remark." She reproached him bitterly. "So sex is a mere nothing, is it? It broke up my life, it deprived me of a husband, my house, and my happiness. It sickened me to death when I learned what you were doing with that other woman.

"Sex to a woman like me means a total and loving commitment and not just casual monkey-mating."

They patched it up for a while, but it was never the same. She glumly surveyed the ruins, writing mournfully that Everett had walked out after a final quarrel over his lady loves. She missed him, being inconsistently human, like any one of her characters.

"I have a beautiful house and it tears my heart out to look at it, for Everett has the most exquisite taste in building and decorating houses." Even in the doldrums, she had a novelist's eye for detail. "There are six bedrooms, a separate guest wing, four bathrooms, a barroom fifty by twenty feet, a dining-room twenty-five by twenty-five, a living-room as large if not larger, a modern kitchen, a large dinette, parquet floors; panelled walls, a large study for me, built of brick and planted gorgeously with flowers. Everett planted them personally.

"Two hours before he left he brought in some lovely pictures—he has a perfect madness for pictures and his taste is impeccable—and a beautiful Chinese screen, and hung the pictures and placed the screen with Jan's help. If he had intended to leave me two hours later, why did he give me these thing and carefully place them, including a magnificent Chinese portable bar all ebony and carved wood and enamel? He even chose the priceless Oriental rugs—we are the only house, I am sure, which has Persian rugs in the kitchen. It is an agonizing mystery to me. Unless all the time he was decorating it for his lady friends. But another thing: He took many cuttings of the ivy I had on my house in Buffalo and carefully brought them here and planted them, and when I would express my admiration he would beam with pride. He told everyone he built and decorated the house 'around Janet.' I can only say that I did everything to please him, wrapped my own life around his and loved him with all my heart, and I thought he was happy with me."

Thoroughly baffled, she made an appointment with a psychic consultant, looking, I suppose, for some tender words of encouragement, some slender ray of hope. She went to her sitting disguised as an ordinary housewife, leaving her jewels at home and arriving in a friend's car. She gave a fictitious name, Mrs. Brown. Nevertheless, her entrance was as dramatic as anything she could have imagined.

"The minute I walked in, the psychic said in a loud voice, clutching her head, 'Oh, you have been marked by tragedy from the day of your birth, God help you! There has been no love in your life, though you have piteously loved and sought for love. Everyone has always exploited you and cheated and lied to you—because you want love, and they pretend to give it to you for their own gain.'

"A neighbor went with me, and she stared with her mouth open and said, 'Mrs. Brown (me) is a very lucky person! You are wrong, Madam.' But Madam said, 'I see her aura, stained with the blood of her heart, and her tears, and I am never mistaken.' She then went on to tell me about my parents, my children, my husbands. She was correct in every detail to my amazement. The neighbor just gawked incredulously, for she knows nothing about me, and once she protested to Madam and said, 'No one could endure what you are telling Mrs. Brown about herself.' To which Madam answered, 'He whom God loves He chasteneth.' ''

At this point, nothing of a personal nature seemed to go well. One of the delights of her life had been her relationship with her daughter Judy. And now that appeared to have soured as well. During Marcus's lifetime a trust from a substantial portion of Janet's royalties had been established in his behalf, resulting in a sizable estate at his death.

Marcus's share went first to Janet, then, eventually, to their daughter. But Judy wanted her share now and had brought an action to get it. It was a crushing blow to a doting mother.

"You think you have troubles?" she wrote. "My darling daughter Judy is suing me for twenty-five percent of all my royalties, as part of her father's estate. In short, I work hard to give Marcus's estate forty-five percent of my royalties, and she wants his share of that. She has served me with a Summons and Complaint."

Judy bothered her more than she let on. The thought that her beloved daughter could sue her seemed to negate love itself, for Judy had always been her favorite.

"If Judy were to knock on the door tomorrow all would be forgiven," said the older Peggy. "Judy has always been Number One."

She was still smarting over Everett's defection when another blow fell. Lee Barker died after a brief illness, and she lost a dear friend and counsellor. I felt the loss as well, for he had played a large role in whatever success I had. I missed his sure touch, his humor, his orderly mind, his rare acumen, and, above all, his honesty. Once, when he suggested that Double-

day take over my agency role, I asked whose side he would
take in a conflict between Doubleday and myself. He answered
with a smile:

"Doubleday's, of course."

He had been a major factor in Janet's success. She had
been at the crossroads when he became her editor, encouraging
her *Dear and Glorious Physician*. Her two previous books,
Tender Victory in 1956 and *The Sound of Thunder* in 1957,
had not been the blockbusters of the past, and she received
only a relatively small advance for *Dear and Glorious Physician*. It was almost like starting over, and she was fortunate to
have an editor who, though unsung, was clearly the peer of
Max Perkins. He had an unerring eye for plot structure and
character development. "Know the beginning and the end,"
he would say, "and the middle will take care of itself."

His criticisms were always specific. He sent her massive
letters, going over a manuscript page by page, chapter by
chapter. Knowing that Janet did not like her work cut or revised, he would suggest passages or chapters that then grew
from her own imagination. Invariably, he sensed the area in
which she could turn on the tap that controlled the incredible
flow of her narrative.

But even more than his technical skill, he gave her the
moral support needed by every novelist, working alone,
haunted by the lurking fear of drying up like the late Scott
Fitzgerald and others. Janet was no stranger to this fear. For
she had reached a block with her book on the Mother of
Christ, to sublimate this somewhat with her thoughts on
Judas.

Barker had been her personal counsellor, seeing her
through Marcus's illness and the break with Everett. His had
always been a good shoulder to cry on. Now, with a deep sense
of loss, she was moved to write pessimistically, her outlook
colored by her own recent disenchantment:

"I was terribly shocked to hear of Lee's sudden death. I
do not pity him, for he is out of this frightful world once and
for all, but I do pity his wife who loved him so dearly. If

Everett had died and I had known nothing, I should be mourning him in peace, deluded to the end, and would have risen to fight again. Now I wish I were where Lee is, wherever that is.''

This self-pitying mood, I knew, would pass. There was too much yet to be done, too much to give the millions who would reflect in awe on the remarkable drama she distilled from the past and marvel where it all came from.

Glory and the Lightning, the outgrowth of her regressions on Pericles and Aspasia, was the last book she did with Barker. It followed by a year our own *Search for a Soul—The Psychic Lives of Taylor Caldwell*, a book he enjoyed, thinking it explained a lot of what Janet was all about.

"I wonder," he had mused, with a whimsical smile, "If there is such a place as Melina, a place where we go and rest, and await our return.''

If there was, he richly deserved that rest. He was a rare man, an editor who cherished his writers.

Chapter Thirteen

JUDAS

AFTER a turbulent three years, she finally returned to "frostbitten" California. She was sitting, with two sweaters on, in the kitchen of my house overlooking the Pacific, pondering anew how it could be so cold when the sun was constantly shining.

"How do you stand it?" she said.

Harold Critoph, a Buffalo contractor who had flown out from the frozen East with her, chuckled over his coffee.

"We left three feet of snow and she wonders how you can stand it."

She was again morose. The divorce from Everett was finalized, but it had not killed her affection for him. Indeed, she had just come from his sickbed, nursing him through a serious illness.

She was still productive, nearing completion of *Ceremony of the Innocent*, to be published the following year, 1976. She didn't think of any book as autobiographical, except for *On Growing Up Tough*, which was a scathing attack on the liberal community and more commentary than autobiography. However, I thought I could pick her out in *Ceremony* as the nubile Ellen, whose slim girlishness was enough to distract an elderly minister in the middle of his Sunday sermon.

She didn't agree. "That could be anybody. You know how girls are today."

But it wasn't today.

"She had red hair," I said, having seen portions of the manuscript. "And she was a scullery maid."

She shrugged indifferently.

"I plead innocent. I never appealed to men of the cloth."

With all her fretting and emotional setbacks, she still looked as well, at seventy-five, as she ever had, and she was still being the prophet. She pushed her newspaper away and puffed on the inevitable cigarette with a distant look.

"China and the United States will yet team up against the Russian monster," she said, "for the Bear has a voracious appetite and will not stop until he is stopped.

"And mark my word," she added gravely, "Islam shall rise again. I should have done my book on Saladin, for the world should have some understanding about the militancy of the Moslem movement." She laughed ironically. "Meanwhile, we squander our energies reducing the productive to poverty and giving what they have earned to those who refuse to work. It's Atlantis all over again."

Harold and I looked at her curiously.

"Is this more of your psychic prophecy?" he teased.

"Laugh if you like, but remember when it happens."

Harold was not easily thrown off.

"Too bad you can't pick your husbands with ESP," he said.

"I did," she said, "I just didn't look for the conclusion. I didn't want to see it. That's the problem when the problem is close to one."

She had tuned into Everett's state of health from the start. And when he became ill she saw it at once, even before he was aware of his own discomfort. The first inkling of its seriousness came during a cruise they took soon after their marriage. They had been playing checkers in the ship's game room, when, suddenly, she heard a woman's voice say, "My son has cancer. Make him see a doctor at once."

"I was so startled," she recalled, "that I looked around for her and was surprised at seeing no one. And then, just as clearly as before, I heard her say, 'I died of cancer and so I know.'"

When Everett confirmed his mother had died in this

fashion, she burst into hysterics and made him promise he would see a doctor. He was examined as soon as possible. And, to her despair, that was what it was.

She looked at us imploringly.

"How do you account for these things? I can't credit their reality until they happen. It is devastating to be like this."

Harold refused to take her mood seriously.

"How are you with the horses?" he asked.

She didn't appear to hear him, turning to me with a frown.

And then, in the same prophetic mood, squinting a little, she said, "You don't realize it, but the book you do about me will assure your fame."

"I've already written our book," I said.

As a matter of fact, *Search* had done very well, becoming a controversial subject of conversation and stimulating interest in Janet's old books. It also did well financially, and, auctioned off as a paperback, had brought a sizable sum.

But this was not the book she had in mind.

"That was all right," she said, "But it should be something more conclusive which will give people hope." She sighed. "God knows, they need it."

That brought me back to my previous complaint.

"In disavowing reincarnation in your epilogue," I said, "You disappointed a good many people who want to believe death is not the end. And yet you can imply in almost the same breath that you were the Empress of Atlantis."

"So that's who you are," said a roguish Critoph, "and I thought all the time you were a Buffalo housewife."

She grimaced and threw the newspaper at him.

The book on Atlantis was finished, and she had no feeling about who published it. "It's really your book," she said with her usual generosity.

Having left Doubleday after Barker's death, I offered *Romance of Atlantis* to William Morrow, a small but excellent publisher. They accepted it readily enough.

Later that evening, when the irreverent Harold was off on

an errand, she picked up on my earlier remark about Atlantis.

"I don't know what's happening," she said, "but I keep having these dreams about Atlantis. And as I look back a hundred years or so"—she smiled at her own facetiousness—"I'm beginning to think that maybe I dreamed it all up when I was a kid."

In these new dreams of the storied continent whole scenes unfolded with an overwhelming reality. They left her with a strange feeling of disquiet. It was ancient Greece—and Florence—again, but this time there was some fond remembrance as well.

In the first dream she saw the towering white colonnade of the palace in which she had "lived," and shimmering gardens more grandiose than anything in life.

"I walked through the gardens seeing the caged birds behind their golden bars, the peacocks stalking the grass, the pit in which squirmed captured reptiles of a breed unknown to us moderns. I saw the liquid golden sea below the palace. I saw the tumbling and rising forest of white stone of my capital city which lay below and above my palace, climbing the great volcanic mountains which surrounded this area. I could even smell the scent of strange flowers and see huge trees with amethyst and blue blossoms the size of our present sunflowers. They were as familiar to me as my present house and its gardens. There were fountains of gilded marble, singing, and red gravel paths winding through beds of shrubs I did not know, all blooming and scented, and endless statues."

She was conscious of a profound emotional distress as she left the garden to stroll back to the colonnade. "I did not wonder at it. I knew what it was: the suffering of 'disprized love,' as Hamlet had mentioned. I was secretely in love with the Emperor Signar of Althrustri. I did not know which was causing me the more anguish—the love I felt for a man I knew I should hate and have quietly murdered, or my love for Atlantis. I knew I must have him killed—yet his nation was now far more powerful than mine. I finally concluded that it would be best for me to die. I knew, in my dream, that he had accepted my younger sister as his bride, and that, too, agonized me."

She awoke feeling the sadness and frustration of her yearning for Signar. It was so intense that she could not get back to the present for an hour or so.

"I felt that somewhere Atlantis still existed, as did Signar, and I had the most terrible urge to look for them both and to tell Signar that I loved him, though I was convinced that he detested me. When I finally realized it was only a dream, I was both relieved and desolated. But I could still hear echoes of Signar's voice in every room of my house."

A week later she dreamed again of Atlantis and Signar in a festive scene marred by the first hint of a volcanic calamity. "I had given a feast for Signar and my sister on an immense gilded raft moored in the harbor. The floor was paved with rugs of intense hues, and there were gemmed tubs of exotic small trees set about and tables covered with cloths of silver. Above the harbor was my palace glittering white in the sun and the vast forest of climbing white stone of my capital city. The raft was thronged with men I knew well, gaily dressed, with garlands on their heads. The water was sprinkled with blossoms but had a curious sulphuric odor. The volcanic mountain immediately above my city wore a pennant of fluttering scarlet smoke, and it made me dimly anxious. But above all, my torment over Signar prevailed. He was sitting on a divan with my sister and boldly caressing her, and I could not endure it. My imperial pennants swayed and snapped in an unseasonably hot breeze, and I could actually feel the perspiration on my forehead and a sense of foreboding.

"Then Signar rose and approached me, smiling in the mocking manner to which I had become accustomed. He saluted me facetiously, and I wanted both to murder and to embrace him. I hurriedly said to him, 'I feel that I shall never again see this aspect of my beloved city.'"

Signar looked at the solemn mountains and peaceful sky and wrily inquired if she was sick.

"Yes, I am sick of an old sickness, and I fear I will die of it."

The dreams continued, but it was no longer Atlantis she dreamed of. Atlantis had disappeared, with all the millions of people Salustra had loved despite their venality and indolence. "I saw a strange land, hot, tropical, with lavender mountains and enormous fronded forests which stretched into infinity. I knew it was a new land and had no inhabitants except for the few of us who had survived the demolition of Altantis. The sea was a strange sea I had never seen before. There was a vast silence everywhere except for the raucous shrieking of birds alien to my experience, great colored birds with huge, hooked beaks, and very small monkeys, and catlike animals of a large size, and cattle—if they were cattle—with twisted horns and shaggy coats. The odors of this land were overpoweringly unique to me, some aromatic, some unpleasant, some strenuously sweet with a hot sweetness. Insects filled the green and shining air, insects for which I had no name.

"But though I sorrowed and wept for Atlantis, I also experienced a joy almost too intense for bearing, for Signar was with me and I knew he loved me as I loved him. Our attendants had built us huts of gray curling bark. I was not Empress any longer, nor was Signar Emperor. We had labored with our people to establish ourselves in this green, hot land with the curiously hued mountains. Our clothing was primitive and our hands as calloused and worn as those of our people. But we were joyful and at peace. I dreamed I was pounding some nameless grain in a wooden bowl, kneeling, and Signar came to me, touched me gently on the head and said, 'This is our empire.' He bent to kiss me and I knew such delight that I closed my eyes—and woke up."

None of this was at that time in my book, which I had refined and honed, keeping in mind the central theme of a people destroyed by a pattern of conduct which was anathema to God. Obviously, she was speaking now about the breakup of Atlantis and the dispersal of its survivors to Greece, Egypt, and other lands as touched on by Plato centuries before. She could only speculate where these visions came from, bringing with them a feeling of *deja vu* that did not readily fade away.

"The dreams were more vivid than my present reality, more poignant, more agonizing, and more joyful. They haunted me, coloring my whole existence, and I felt deprived and filled with ancient longing."

The lingering impressions clouded her waking hours. I could see that, for the moment, she was into it again.

She sat silent for a while, looking out on the gray ocean, then turned to me with a speculative eye.

"You know, of course, who Signar was?"

"I don't have the slightest idea," I said. "I thought it was all a child's imagination."

"I thought as much once," she said, "but not anymore. There was a definite impression who Signar was. And when I awoke this time I knew for sure."

She looked at me with the faintest smile.

"Don't you know? After all, look what you have done with the book, and the sureness with which you have written, keeping that which had to be kept and throwing out that which was extraneous."

Her smile broadened.

"It was only a hunch then. Now I know."

I saw the drift at last and began to laugh.

"It's no laughing matter," she said, drawing herself up a little, "and don't go calling yourself Siggie."

I was not exactly floored by this revelation. In fact, it didn't faze me in the least. I had been Robert Browning and Branwell Brontë, at one and the same time, so why not Signar of Althrustri?

I didn't know what to properly believe. Yet I felt there was a deep and strong bond between us. For there were times when I empathized with her so intensely that whenever she experienced sadness, as with Judy's suit, I felt sad as well. And with her marriage to Everett, I rejoiced, too, even knowing he was hardly a good marriage risk and certainly no Estanbul. Somewhere, somehow, at some disputed barricade, perhaps, our pasts had crossed. That I knew, and I knew that she knew as much, or more.

Some progress appeared to have been made. Having spoken of past lives as if they were actualities, I felt she had definitely committed herself on reincarnation and could no longer disavow it.

"As you know," I said, "the Pharisees believed in reincarnation, and Jesus himself asked the disciples who men thought He was before, and when they replied Elias or Elijah or one of the older prophets, he said that was not He but John the Bapitst. What were they speaking of but reincarnation?"

She shrugged, incomprehensibly holding back.

"They may have been speaking broadly of the spiritual influence of these prophets. We assume too much, not considering that *X*, the Unknown, may be the true solution."

"When you say someone is a spiritual entity, you still haven't disposed of the idea that he has survived and is, figuratively speaking, in a new environment, in a new suit of clothes."

She thought about this for a moment.

"Why do we insist that everything be neatly packaged and labeled, when only the good Lord knows what He intended and how he intended it?" She smiled. "He may not believe in reincarnation at all."

But weren't Darios, Estanbul, even Lucifer all testimonials to a singular continuity of life?

"I'm not quite sure of the game plan," she said. "Not like all the Anthonys and Cleopatras who glory in that mark of vanity. And I don't think we should get into reincarnation in the *Judas* book. It would distract from the central idea—Judas's challenge and Christ's response."

"Then you do want to do the book?"

She nodded. "But it must be offered first to Doubleday, since it was Lee Barker's idea. I wouldn't want to upset the dears."

And so our agreement, much like our *Atlantis* pact, was drawn up in a paragraph or two, fewer than a hundred words, without the fanfare of lawyers or agents. Harold witnessed our signatures with a flourish.

As she folded the agreement, Janet put a finger to her lips and said, "Mum's the word, boys."

Harold gave her a puzzled look. "And why is that?"

She whispered, almost stealthily:

"Because certain people do not want this to happen."

"Don't you think," said the unflappable Harold, "that you're old enough to do what you want?"

"Now, don't be impertinent, Childe Harold," she said.

"And who is opposed?" I asked.

"My agent, William Morris, for one; my new business manager [succeeding Jan Robinson], and Doubleday."

"Then let's not do it," I said.

Her eyes flashed. "I don't let anybody tell me what to write."

I knew she liked the idea of "family," feeling comfortable in a continuing personal relationship with Doubleday through their new editor-in-chief, Stewart (Sandy) Richardson. But of course a book done by us jointly relieved her of any contractual commitments in her name alone.

Living three thousand miles apart, it was necessary to establish some common concept, to make sure we were on the same track. "I must stress," she said, "that Judas was not Christ's adversary, though he appears that way historicallly. And you must remember at all times the Jewishness of the Messiah and the Apostles, for without recognizing this tradition none of the drama can be properly understood."

I would do the first draft. She would go over it, adding and subtracting, revising as she liked. With first drafts, revisions, and rewrites the typewriter keys would be tapped two to three million times before the book was completed. It took some resolution to hit that first key, knowing how many more movements it would take to produce 120,000 words or so, not to mention giving the reader a unique reading experience. Even with her startling new concept of Judas, Christ was still the protagonist of our book, the center around whom all disciples revolved.

She had strong impressions about the Holy Land. Yet she

had never enjoyed Jerusalem (where the Magdalene was stoned), uneasy all the while she was there. She preferred to browse the rolling Galilean hills, for there she felt a peace and security she experienced almost nowhere else.

Mary was still not coming well, and she was anxious to get started on our project, voicing various objections to our working title, *I, Judas,* thinking it simpler to handle the action from the vantage point of an omnipresent third person.

I had thought it would be easier to portray Judas through seeing everything directly through his eyes. His search for salvation through Jesus, his distortion of Christ's mission, his belated recognition of his own error, with an agonizing remorse. All this would be the more effective, I felt, if we could but perceive the seduction of his own mind.

"How dramatic their first meeting must have been," I said. "For certainly Jesus, who knew His own fate, must have known He was picking His eventual betrayer as His twelfth Apostle—oddly the only Judean among eleven Galileans."

Her eyes caught mine for a moment and she wagged a finger under my nose. "Never Judas's betrayal. Remember, Christ was betrayed by the times and circumstance. Actually, He died on the Cross so people would be exalted by His suffering and the promised Resurrection. If you recall, in John 10, He said no man took His life, that He died to fulfill his own destiny."

The thought of Judas telling the story continued to disturb her sense of propriety. And, too, it had no historical justification. She frowned over it, then suddenly her face lit up. She had a solution. "Of course," she said. "Judas left a diary, which vanished for ages and finally turned up in Alexandria, and then vanished again, only to be recently found."

So positive was she that I inquired, "Is there any proof of this?"

There was a flutter of hands.

"Why should Matthew and John be the only ones of the twelve to do a chronicle of their Master's life?"

She closed her eyes, apparently visualizing again, and

then said with animation, "I will do a prologue describing the diary."

"And if the diary turns up," saucily put in Harold Critoph, who had been sitting awe-stricken till now, "neither of you will have to write the book."

She gave him a devastating look, then quickly made her points. She had strong feelings about Jesus the Man, as well as the Godhead. "Now don't make Him some meek, mealy-mouthed creature without resolution or courage. He was an angry man as well as a peaceful one. If we show Him as an all-forgiving pusillanimous shepherd of the flock, they'll flay us alive from every pulpit in the country."

Harold wore an amused smile. "That should make it a best-seller."

She patted his hand affectionately. "Harold is incorrigible. I should have dropped him off the plane en route."

I had some ideas of my own.

I had always thought of Christ and forgiveness in the same breath, and I did not see how I could present Him any other way. She shook her head and said with uncharacteristic severity:

"As between you and me it is pretty well established who is the Biblical authority."

I had no quarrel with this. But that night I pored over the Bible, looking for a dimly remembered passage, and was finally rewarded:

"Then came Peter to Him, and said, Lord, how oft shall my brother sin against me, and I forgive him, till seven times?"

"Jesus saith unto him, I say not unto thee, Until seven times, but, Until seventy times seven."

I carefully wrote this down.

She was sipping her noontime orange juice, and Harold was fixing the coffee when I sat down and studied my scrap of paper with the most obvious concentration.

"What have you there?" she inquired, as I had expected she would.

Meticulously, I quoted chapter and verse—Matthew 18:21—and then added with a flourish, "Now, as between you and me you are the unquestioned Biblical authority, but as to Mark and Matthew—?"

She snorted disdainfully. "You know exactly what I meant. Make Christ the firebrand He was. We would not be worshipping Him two thousand years later if He wasn't a man all men could admire and aspire to be like."

Harold clapped his hands enthusiastically. "Bravo, Janet," he cried. "And the hell with everybody."

Janet gave him a scathing look and turned back to me. "I don't envy you," she said, "you have a long chore ahead. We writers hate to write. It is an arduous discipline, and we are really lazy at heart. Moreover, you can get swallowed up in your characters and have no life of your own. This is something only writers know about. In Buffalo they think I 'play' on my typewriter 'and the money pours out.'"

Even with the first line still unwritten on Judas, she was brimming with ideas for other books we might do, such as the Daughters of Lilith, concerning the critical point of change in the fortunes of the great courtesans of history: Cleopatra, Theodora, Zenobia, the Empress of China, Catherine the Great, Madam Pompadour, Josephine, Lady Hamilton, DuBarry.

I had never heard of Lilith before, but as she reeled off the names of these exalted sirens I groaned, thinking of the research.

"It would take a lifetime."

She gave me an incredulous look.

"I'll start you off with two or three. All you do is turn to the encyclopedia, absorb a little factual information, then let your imagination roam. Just show how their lives were turned around at the moment of crisis. Take Theodora. She was a lowly prostitute, and in a moment of despair, destitute, friendless, thinking of suicide, she kneeled and prayed to a nameless God. And the spirit of Lilith responded, enabling her to turn her life around and become the greatest figure in the

Roman Empire."

All I knew about Theodora was that she had married the Emperor Justinian in the sixth century and became, through her resoluteness, the supreme authority in the Roman Empire.

I looked at Janet uncertainly .

"I suppose there was some spiritual awakening."

"Hell, no, she was just told where to go and stand in the street. When Justinian came by in his litter, his eyes fell on her. One look, that was all it took, for centuries of slumbering love went into that glance."

It sounded intriguing indeed.

"And who is this Lilith?" I asked.

"You don't know?" She quoted loosely: "Before Eve, there was another daughter of God, and her name was Lilith.

"Legend has it that she was the first wife of Adam. And in the ancient Talmudic tradition she was a spirit that worked her wiles nocturnally, capricious and sometimes malicious, but always on the side of women."

Thinking of all the work on Judas, I could muster no enthusiasm for Lilith.

"Don't give up so easily," she rallied. "I have been sorting out notes about the great concubines of history—all very interesting and delightful women, which is more than you can say for wives. And when I get home I'll send it all to you for Lilith. I'll also write the foreword, if you wish. And we can discuss your progress."

I was again struck by her thoughtfulness, but the project had no appeal for me.

At her suggestion, I found myself meditating more and more. I visualized the streets of Jerusalem and actually began to see a fair-haired, blue-eyed Jesus followed by His disciples, speaking on the wayside to them and others. I saw Him in the Temple, fearlessly bearding the High Priest in the Court of the Gentiles (which the Bible had no record of) and berating the money-changers. I saw Him with John the Baptist, and with Judas, who had sought the Messiah in John and found Him in Jesus.

I saw all this and more, and though I mentioned none of it, I saw Janet watching me from time to time, as if she understood the dramatic changes taking place inside me. There was little she missed.

We had many more discussions about Judas, and she turned over some notes from the past. "Just things that came to me," she said, "which brings me to another book I'd like you to do about my experiences with ESP, visions, 'memories,' happenings, the 'people' I observed and talked with as a child. I always felt quite disoriented because of the vividness of the things I saw, the warnings I was given, the frequent associations with Darios—who isn't speaking to me at present, by the way—and of the prophecies that passed through me."

She then added, typically, "And no royalties for me. I can't afford any more income."

Harold was visibly impressed by Janet's openness. "I've never seen you this way with anybody else," he said.

"She thinks that I'm Signar," I said with a smile, "and that she's Salustra."

Not having seen the manuscript, Harold only scratched his head in bewilderment.

Aside from this fancied connection, I still had no clear idea why she encouraged our collaborations. She certainly didn't need me. She was a literary light with a following in the millions. And I was doing very well in my own way, so it was not a case of helping an indigent friend. It had to be something else.

One day, unexpectedly, I got a clue. Dorothy Vallas, a Los Angeles medium who idolized the novelist, volunteered a psychic reading just so that she could get to know what made Janet tick.

"I'm sure," she said, "that she goes back a long ways."

Because Janet thought trance mediums ridiculously spooky, Dorothy promised not to go into trance. "I will merely close my eyes to concentrate better and bring in my spirit guides. They do the work for me." We told her nothing.

She meditated briefly, then gave Janet a curious look, as though seeing her for the first time.

"My guide tells me that you were of a Judean family from Galilee in Jesus' time and that you knew Him." She turned to me with the same odd expression. "Jess was a writer, or scribe, at the same time, and you knew each other. You were both also aware of the Christ, and Jess had the opportunity then to write down an experience you were very much involved with emotionally, but he only scoffed. And now when you, still pursuing the past, wish him to write something, he feels karmically obligated to drop everything and do your bidding." She looked up, shaking her head a little. "Does any of this make sense?"

And so there it was, Salustra and Signar and a couple of Judeans who knew Jesus together. However absurd or pretentious this might seem, I could see now that her subconscious mind had mulled over this possibility many times.

The reading had given us both something to think about. Janet seemed unusually impressed.

"I don't care for mediums as a rule," she said later, "psychics are another matter, but Vallas knew what she was talking about." She looked at me closely. "Now without committing yourself on reincarnation, have you ever felt you lived at that time?"

I had some feelings of *deja vu.*

"I had a vivid impression of seeing Christ, once, but never knew how valid it was. Perhaps it was wishful thinking."

She could be jocular even when most serious. "Tell me," she grinned, "how do we get out of this rut?"

There didn't seem to be anything more to say. Anything else would have been anticlimactic. I could only shrug.

The fact that she was to do a major novel with me caused some consternation at Doubleday, concerned that she might be lured to another publisher. And so she wrote reassuringly to editor-in-chief Sandy Richardson.

"Lee Barker," she explained, "thought it would be a fine combination—Jess with his reportorial ability and objective point of view and I from the contemplative and religious point of view. Moreover, it was tentatively decided Jess would do the main work on *Judas*. This was discussed with Lee long before he died. From time to time, Jess would bring up the subject, but something else was always crowding my writing time, and so it hung there for a number of years.

"After mutual discussions about poor Lee, we got to talking about the long-projected *I, Judas*. I finally entered into an informal agreement with the understanding that he was to do all the drudgery, all the research, and I was to approve what he writes. In the agreement there is a prominent paragraph that Doubleday is to get the very first opportunity to reject or accept. Also, as Jess will be doing at least seventy percent of the work, the book would be handled through his agent (Scott Meredith). Only in the event that Doubleday rejects the book would Jess's present publishers be contacted. That is the full agreement."

She assured Richardson she was sending on *Ceremony of the Innocent*, and plotting still another novel. "Another book for Doubleday is fighting with the present book in my mind. The next book is complaining that the time for the present one is up."

I was again struck by the zest with which she approached her work. In the few years since Marcus's death she had done *Captains and the Kings*, *Glory and the Lightning*, was finishing up *Ceremony of the Innocent*, and already structuring her next effort, *Bright Flows the River*, while dealing with *I, Judas*.

We communicated regularly during the maturation of *I, Judas*. She provided an endless flow of information that helped me visualize the Palestinian countryside and its troubled people as I might never have otherwise. She read over carefully what I had written, offered a suggestion here and there, expressing satisfaction with the way Judas's character was developing. "Just as Christ is Everyman in the nobility of His aspirations and His supreme faith," she observed, "so is Judas Everyman in his nameless fears and lack of faith."

She asked what more she could do, and when I suggested

the epilogue, she said she would do it on the Resurrection.

"It is significant," said Janet, "that the Magdalene was the first to see Him after he vanished from the sepulchre. That was because she loved Him most."

"And what makes you so sure of that?" I asked.

She frowned and her eyes had that familiar faraway look.

"I know—because I can close my eyes and see her now, fallen to her knees, battered by the stones, looking up to Him in reverence, her heart bleeding from the love she bore Him."

Chapter Fourteen

BIBLICALLY HERS

JANET was concerned that our book in no way dispute the Bible. "For if we don't accept the New Testament intact," she said, "then what do we accept about Christianity? It is not for us to pick and choose."

I sent her questions, and she responded immediately, making her answers crystal clear and almost lyrical in their eloquence. I had the feeling that her authority was more than scholarly. She managed to inject her own irreverent opinions, but essentially she adhered to dogma, explaining it as I had never heard it explained.

She had a more elaborate answer now for my question about the apparent belief in reincarnation by Christ's disciples.

"When Jesus said one must be 'born again' to enter Heaven, He meant—according to the Bible—that one must be born of the Holy Spirit, that is a spiritual rebirth in one's present body. And that is what Christ was referring to when He spoke of 'being born again.' He honestly didn't mean reincarnation. But the ancient Jews, especially the Pharisee sect, did believe in reincarnation, and that is why they asked Christ if he was the spiritual embodiment of Elias or Jeremiah."

She was anxious to see me, for *I, Judas,* and to have somebody to share her own writing problems with. She had finished *Ceremony of the Innocent* and was not quite sure of the result, what with brooding about Judy and still nursing the declining Everett out of a residual sense of duty. *Ceremony* was more somber than most of her novels and did not have the optimism of some, but it still had a way of pulling the reader into the web she so intriguingly spun.

"When you have finished a book," she wrote, "do you despair, thinking it lousy? I do, every time. After I finished *Ceremony*, then came the dull and sweating task of editing it, cutting out the sneaky cliches and the hyperbole, and rewriting in wretchedness. Well, it's all ready, finally—550 pages of it. On reading it over many times, with my blue pencil in hand, I decided it had some merit."

She had liked what little she had seen of *Judas* and anticipated it would receive a critical, if not hostile, reception. "The critics like stereotypes, which they understand, and they don't approve of me. *Publishers Weekly* doesn't like me. Neither does the *Kirkus Report*, which loved me dearly up to the time Judy and her husband played bridge with one of the critics, and Judy beat her. Since then the Kirkus people slam my books monotonously. Moral: Don't let your daughter play bridge with an editor of a critical review."

Romance of Atlantis had been published, here and abroad, and was brought out in paperback by the very house which had turned it down before I revised it. She enthused over it as though she had never seen it before. "It is your book, now," she said generously.

She had plunged into *Bright Flows the River*, but had assured me nothing took precedence over *Judas*. "I have been taking massive notes about Our Book. We can get together and rapidly finish it. The contract calls for a short book—a concerto, not an opus, so I think two months more at the most will do it. I have even decided on the style. Three thousand miles separating collaborators seems a silly way to write a book. How about you coming to Buffalo and working in my study at your own typewriter all day, while I pound on mine all night? Then we can show each other our daily output—or is it input?"

Doubleday had been given an outline and had turned it down. So it was put up on auction by agent Scott Meredith and went to Atheneum and New American Library, for an advance larger than any she had received up to this point.

Taking her advice, I soon had several chapters to take to Buffalo with me. I discovered on my arrival a conspiratorial air in the household. Janet herself greeted me at the door and solemnly warned that I not mention the project to anybody.

"How do I explain this?" I said, mystified, indicating the manuscript jammed under one arm.

"It's nobody's business," she said, "and don't listen to my lawyers or my business agent. I don't give a damn what they say."

I noticed several strangers skulking about the big house, but Janet made sure I didn't get into any extended conversations with them. Jan Robinson arrived for cocktails with her husband, not appearing to mind at all having been replaced by a man she had recommended.

We dined out that night, with a large company of Janet's friends, and I studiously avoided any explanation of my presence. I noticed Janet beaming approvingly. What seemed like an ordinary visit had become a mission of intrigue and mystery.

Even when we were alone later, the air of secrecy prevailed.

"We will trade manuscripts," she said, reaching out for the envelope I had brought with me. Then, taking my hand, she led me into her study and with a furtive look brought out one hundred typewritten pages of the book she wanted to make her crowning achievement.

"You are the first person," she said, "permitted to even glance at these pages."

It was the saga of Mary, the Mother of Jesus, and of course the Christ story through Mary's eyes.

Recalling how Barker had mentioned her block on this book, I took myself off to a corner and settled down to review the pages she had given me. I read carefully, slowly, finding myself irresistibly drawn into the deep recesses of a mother's eternal mind. The pages brimmed with tender emotion. They mirrored not only her mingled sorrow and exaltation at His birth, but the bright expectancy of immortal maternity stirring in her breast. She saw it all before it took form, from the bare,

cold manger in Bethlehem to the Cross at Calvary, and
beyond. She was a compelling figure, radiant, proud, not to be
pitied or commiserated with, enduring through time as the
Mother figure for an expectant mankind.

I turned the last page, letting it all slip away for a
moment. I had seen the Christ through the clear eyes of the
person who knew Him first, growing as He grew Himself to
teach that death was the last enemy to be vanquished.

In these brief pages of Taylor Caldwell's I saw the
unfolding of man's supreme moment, rich with the promise of
eternity, And with it came an understanding of why God had
permitted His only begotten Son to die on the Cross. For it was
an unforgettable moment symbolizing Christ's message of
everlasting life. Had he lived to the full ripeness of an Isaiah or a
Jeremiah, with a gray beard and a bent frame, dying in bed, He
would never have been the compelling figure that inspired man
through the ages. I knew all this, not knowing how I knew it.

As I was thinking this, Janet came hurtling through the
door, waving my manuscript. Her eyes were sparkling. She
had stormed through two hundred pages while I was reading
half of that.

She took my hand and pressed it.

"Great, great, great," she cried. "My God, the research
you did." She drew herself back a little to look at me, as if seeing me for the first time. "You were always the journalist, but
now you have gone to a new dimension. This is superb. You
have outdone yourself. There is nothing to do but go on as you
have. Do nothing to stop the flow."

Suddenly her mood changed, and she became the gruff,
hardbitten woman of business she chose to appear at times.

"We should make pots," she said.

As I shrugged, she looked at me almost anxiously.

"Well?" she said, her eyes dropping to the pages in my
hand. "What is the verdict?"

"It's the best thing you have written," I said. "You must
put everything aside and finish it."

She sighed and gave me a troubled look.

"I've tried," she said, "but I'm stuck. I don't know whether it's Judy's suit, my miserable love life, or having nothing to work for, but I can't break through."

There had been no Darios in the dark hours of the night, no dazzling wall of light, no Estanbul, nothing to hearten her and light the way for her tripping fingers.

"It will come," I said, encouragingly. "It is a book readers will treasure as long as Christianity endures."

As she still looked troubled, frowning a little, I said, "By the way, your manuscript has given me a new chapter for *Judas*."

She gave me an inquiring look.

"Mary's recollections of Jesus as a youth."

She seemed pleased. "I'm glad you finally got something out of me."

Leaving this household of mystifying intrigue, concocted, I suspected, out of her high sense of drama, I went back to California to finish my end of *Judas*, heartened by her promise to visit me before long. She wrote frequently, still lamenting her loneliness. But she had no thought of going back to Everett. "Once something is gone, it is gone. It is easier to build afresh, than rebuild on a weakened foundation."

Psychics had foreseen another marriage for her, but she chose to believe this was amiable fortune-telling. She was happiest married, even when the sparks were flying (or because of it), and she desperately missed the cozy late-hour companionship of "unholy matrimony."

Everett had been company. He was well-read, well-traveled, and could speak knowledgeably of many things, and he had respected her particular genius. Knowing all this, she analyzed herself on one occasion:

"I am one woman who needs the comfort and protection and shelter and love of a man—a house is not a home without a man in it. You know how completely wrapped up I was in Marcus, and how I really had no separate existence. When he died it was as if I had died also. I determined never to love a man to that disastrous stage ever again, and that is why in the past few years I have cultivated the friendship of married men only. I didn't want the agony of loving a man completely again and possibly marrying again, with the resultant and inevitable misery of eventually parting through death. I intended never to have a deep soul-destroying love again. But I overlooked my innate nature, the fact that I am a very dependent woman, dependent on men, and that I cannot refrain from loving. So, of course, I came to disaster."

Wherever she turned she saw human treachery and deception. It was no wonder her books were full of rogues and ruffians, nor was it surprising that she had an inordinate affection for the animal known for his loyalty and devotion—whose very name, as she pointed out, spelled God backwards.

She loved my two giant shepherds, whom I had reared from pups, and was distressed that big, lovable Brutus had been killed on the highway. He had been a very special animal, a great heart in a great body. He would come off the beach every morning at precisely five minutes to eight, nose into the living-room, look around tentatively to establish that we were alone, then lay his great head on my lap and insist that I speak to him for five minutes. If I broke off even a few seconds before this time, he would prod me with his big paw. And then at eight sharp, satisfied, he would sally forth on the beach to chase the birds as they skimmed over the waves. Knowing how I felt, she sent a condolence that was a commentary on her own sensibilities.

"I know just how you feel about Brutus, and how sad and inconsolable. I have had pets, from cats to birds to dogs, people far more faithful and loving than humans. I never told you about my parakeet, Timothy, who had much more intelligence than the average human being and with whom I could have—amazingly—a perfectly relevant and understanding conversation. And then there was my boxer, Robert, full of mischief and love and arrogance and humor and egotism, who loved to chase cars—with the predictable results. It doesn't do to love animals so much; the inevitable heartbreak is too much. But then you get heartbreak from humans without the

devotion and, usually, with treachery and betrayal and con-
tempt.''

Judy's suit had put her to the expense and trouble of
defending the action and had made deep inroads on her
psyche. Judy's portrait, once hanging lovingly next to
Marcus's in the foyer, was brought down and put in a closet.
And soon she would talk no more about her.

I urged her to come to California for the three months she
normally spent voyaging around the world. She finally agreed,
and a pleasant condominium was found for her on a golf
course in Palm Springs. This was now early 1977, and her
Ceremony of the Innocent was near the top of the best-seller
list. Sitting in the middle of a golf course she found herself in
the unaccustomed spotlight and was soon signing books by the
hundreds as word spread who she was. Television had
discovered her dramatic whoppers, and she was elated by the
sale of *Captains and the Kings* for a network miniseries. And
no sooner was that arranged than another syndicate purchased
her *Testimony of Two Men*, and still another took options for
two or three others. She was the only author to have two such
miniseries going at once, achieving a new celebrity, particularly among the young, oriented more to the tube than to
print. Many changes had been introduced in the television
version of *Captains and the Kings*, and while critics as well as
associates and friends were horrified by wild sexual scenes not
in the book, she was quite philosophical about it. "That," she
observed drily, "is television."

She didn't watch much of the series; the new scenes
disoriented her, and she couldn't lip-read from the television
screen. But she secretly enjoyed her new and wider celebrity,
finding she couldn't enter a restaurant now without being
mobbed by autograph hunters. The reason for her books not
having been made into theatrical motion pictures now became
clearly apparent. The canvas she drew was vastly too large for
the usual two-hour movie. But a television miniseries of ten or
twelve hours could profit by all the fascinating detail that
made her novels special. And so TV, which bored her, ironic-

ally magnified her popularity and pocketbook.

Ostensibly, she had come out to California to work with me, and she was full of suggestions. Still a stickler on the Bible, she made sure no statement by Christ or the Apostles was bent out of shape in *I, Judas*.

Nevertheless, she pointed out there could be some confusion in interpretation. For sometimes the same word repeated in the Bible, even in the same Gospel, seemed to convey different shades of meaning. The word *begotten*, in John, for instance, applied to Christ's physical birth as the Son of God. In Revelation, by the same Apostle, it seemed to carry an entirely different meaning.

She had a ready explanation. "First, let us understand that Christ thought of all the faithful as the children of God. And John, who spoke of Christ as 'the only begotten of the Father,' meaning God, showed at the same time that Christ, too, had the authority to create sons of God. She quoted from John 1:12:

"But as many as received him [Christ], to them gave he power to become the sons of God, even to them that believe on his name."

She was able to quote almost any Biblical passage at any time. "I don't know why this particular *begotten* stops so many people," she said, "when you consider that God the Creator made billions of planets and everything on them. Obviously, He could create anything He wanted, even to implanting a spirit or form in the womb."

There was still another construction of *begotten*—indicating the rebirth of the spirit, even reincarnation.

"And from Jesus Christ, who is the faithful witness, and the first *begotten* of the dead, and the prince of the kings of the earth, Unto him that loved us and washed us from our sins in his own blood."

Begotten of the dead—what was that but rebirth of the soul?

I had been working rapidly, and before long finished my draft and turned it over to her. With a pleased smile she glanced through it, then put it aside.

All that night a light burned in her bedroom, and about five in the morning I heard a tapping on my door. The door opened a crack, then quickly closed. I awoke later to find the manuscript of *I, Judas* just inside the door, with a note attached.

"The creator of *I, Judas* should be so elated by the grandeur of the book—and its magnificent promise—that he should waste no time in sleep. He should be thinking of his accomplishment—and future ones. As the Bible says, there is a prohibition concerning sleep for the creators."

At breakfast, she kept praising the book. "Marvelous, superb. You have outdone yourself."

I found myself embarrassed.

"Are you trying to get out of doing your share?"

"What is there to do," she replied, "except to write the epilogue?"

She was particularly touched by the imagined visit of Judas and Matthew with the Holy Mother in Nazareth, inspired by her own manuscript on Mary. "You stuck faithfully to the Biblical story of Mary's maternity, and yet you made their questioning and her explanations seem as natural as a newspaper interview."

She turned the pages, observing every once in a while how it must have happened just as I described it. "I particularly like the way you introduce Christ and the Baptist . . . may I read it aloud?"

She read easily, without glasses:

"A solitary figure came slowly over the rise. His arms were swinging evenly, and he moved with a determined stride. There were a handful of pilgrims on the highway from Jericho, but the lone wanderer cut across the desert sands and scrub and headed in a beeline for the ford where the Baptist stood waiting, his eyes on the horizon.

"As he saw John the stranger's stride quickened and he seemed to radiate light. Isaiah had said he would not be comely, but he was beyond comeliness, for his beauty was not of his features. There was an aura almost like a halo that seemed to envelop him and herald his imminence. It dazzled me [Judas] to look directly into his eyes. Their blueness held my own, and I could not have moved at that moment to save my soul. His steady gaze was encompassing, not seeming to vary a shade in expression. And yet there was an indescribable impression of sternness, compassion, love, and resolve without any effort on his part. His face seemed to soften only as he leaned forward and kissed John.

"For a moment a shadow crossed the Baptist's face. He spoke in a low voice. 'We must make haste, for time grows short.'

"The stranger nodded.

"'There will be enough time for what I do.'"

Our discussion seemed to lift Janet's spirits. "It is just the way I would have written it," she said, giving me a little bow as she returned the manuscript with her marginal notes.

Though I had hit the typewriter keys, her conception of Judas and the Bible, and the notes she had compiled over the years, were the heart of the story. She suggested some slight changes and promised to get on with the epilogue. "Anything else I do would only detract. The critics won't like it. As I said, they are comfortable only with stereotypes. But mark my word, one day it will be a classic, and you will be remembered for it."

I was pleased, but I knew the book could not have happened without her.

"I have the epilogue under control," she said. "it was no accident that Mary of Magdala saw Him first after the Resurrection. He knew she would not doubt him."

I was struck now by her use of the name Mary of Magdala, from the regressions, rather than the customary Mary Magdalene. Was she unwittingly adopting an old role stirring about in her subconscious? Wondering, I asked;

"How would it be to have a daughter disappear for years and later discover she was a common prostitute?"

She bridled instantly. "How can you say that? She was

driven to it by circumstance. She had no friends, was cut off from her family, and had this handicap which kept her from marrying. What else was she to do? And the men—what makes them so superior, taking advantage of a poor girl's misfortune?"

She was obviously over-reacting. "You are taking it very personally," I said.

"Only because she's a woman abused."

"Then you don't believe you might have been the mother?"

She gave me a withering glance. "Do I look two thousand years old?"

We did not speak of survival or reincarnation for a while. But one day, at the Palm Springs home of the John Contes, I observed her benignly studying a middle-aged man who had just walked into the room.

"I have met you before," she said, finally, "it was in England."

He gave her a puzzled look. "I was in England as a Rhodes scholar, but I don't remember meeting you."

She laughed. "Oh, no, there were no Rhodes scholars then. This was in 1710," she wagged a finger, "and you were in the Hellfire Club. You were very naughty."

He gulped a little. "If you say so," he said, and with an uneasy look he quickly moved off, shaking his head.

At seventy-seven now, she was dramatic proof that the human will controlled both mind and body. The doctors she met socially in Palm Springs were alarmed by her chain-smoking and bourbon drinking. One physician, not yet forty, solemnly warned her that she would not last six months at this pace.

"Get into my office for a checkup," he insisted. "I see symptoms of acute heart disease. Your tongue is red and your ankles swollen; your breath comes in gasps. Come in before it's too late."

She snorted audibly and then predicted in a loud aside, "I'll outlast that crepe-hanger!"

Six months later the youthful doctor had a severe heart attack and was incapacitated. She solicitously asked if she could send flowers to his hospital room.

Her problem in Palm Springs, as elsewhere, was boredom. She didn't wake up till twilight. so as to avoid the desert's blazing sun, and the resort's vaunted sunshine was wasted on her. However, she vigorously applied herself to the typewriter and emerged triumphantly from her room one evening with a dozen crumpled pages in her hand.

"Here is your epilogue," she said. "It happened during the night."

I sat down and was soon enthralled with Mary of Magdala, seen, I was sure, as only a mother could have known her. I was particularly moved by the scene at Christ's tomb, where with John and Simon Peter she had made the discovery that Christ's body had disappeared from the sepulchre. But then as the others drew off, irresolutely, she peered boldly beyond the mouth of the tomb.

"She saw what neither Simon nor John had seen. She saw the great white figures before her, one sitting at the head of the shelf, the other at the foot, the grave cloths betwen them. They were the figures of men, clothed in shimmering light, but they were larger than men and their faces were beautiful and lofty, far removed from mankind and as still as alabaster. They regarded her in a long silence, while she, paralyzed, could only stare whitely at them.

"Then one spoke, and his voice was like a distant thunder. 'Woman, why do you weep?' His words were compassionate, but his was not a human voice and it evoked unfamiliar echoes.

"She stammered, holding to the side of the aperture, 'Because they have taken away my Lord, and I know not where they have laid him.' Her terror grew, for she was not dealing with anything recognizable; the remote faces affrighted her. A tall dark shadow loomed at her side, and she shrank back, whimpering with fear.

"She heard the voice of a man speaking gently. 'Woman,

why do you weep. Whom do you seek?'

"The voice was full of pity and kindness, but distant, and she thought that he must be one of the gardeners. She tried to control herself but could not speak for a moment or two. At last she could whisper, 'Sir, if you have borne him hence, tell me where you have laid him, and I will take him away.'

"There was a little silence. Mary, without thinking, leaned imploringly toward the shadow, no longer so affrighted.

"Then he said: 'Mary!'

"She could not believe what she had heard, she could not believe who had spoken. She tried to rise but fell back on her knees, her face alight with vivid rapture, her hands clasped, her head thrown back, her mouth shaking.

"'Rabboni!' she cried."

As I finished, there were tears in my eyes; I could not help it.

She looked at me closely. "You weren't at the cave," she said. "They told you about it."

Chapter Fifteen

ETERNALLY YOURS

APPROACHING eighty, very few women have serious thoughts of romance. Nor are they in position to contemplate the crowning achievement of their careers. But Taylor Caldwell was no ordinary person. She lived her life by her own values, held opinions that many quarreled with, without her quarreling with them.

Age had never been a factor in her life, except when she was young. Only then, as she said, because she was born old. As the years passed, bringing fame and riches, she seemed to throw off the mantle of time.

Over the breakfast table, shorn of makeup, clad in an old robe, she said quite seriously, "You've known me for twenty years; do I look any older to you?"

I looked back, taking in the smooth and rosy skin, the tightness about the slender throat, the keen eye, and said quite truthfully:

"You look the same to me."

Her eyebrows tilted upward, always a dangerous sign, and she growled, "Just the same! You mean I don't look any better?"

She was not averse to helping nature along and was almost eighty when she disappeared into a hospital for some minor refurbishing. It was purely elective surgery, and I questioned its necessity, for the years had been kind to her.

And when a concerned friend called her hospital room, inquiring after her, she impishly remarked:

"Tell her I'm having an abortion."

She was dauntless in the face of adversity that would have dismayed Joseph Armagh, the stout-hearted hero of *Captains and the Kings*. Like him, she bent but never broke.

I saw in her a deep, abiding faith, nourished now and then by the murmur of distant voices and the dazzling white light that announced there was still a Darios and Melina, still a haven for the human spirit to replenish itself until it was time to return.

She met life on its own terms, like Corneila, Caroline, Armagh and a host of others who scratched their way to the top in her books.

"As long as you're warm and breathing," she told me, "you're alive. And if you're alive, do something about it."

And so it was no surprise to me, or any of her friends, that with three marriages behind her, she planned to "commit matrimony" a fourth time. It would be her second marriage as a septuagenarian.

In Palm Springs she had met a younger man, debonair, handsome, divorced. They were drawn together by an interest in the metaphysical. And she kept thinking of him when she got back to Buffalo. He seemed kind and considerate and was a great fan of hers.

On her next visit to California, this man, Robert Prestie, cheerfully flew to Buffalo to bring her back. The sixty-year-old Prestie, a realtor well-known in Palm Springs social circles, was more than ready to abandon his life there and make her life his life. It seemed an ideal arrangement. But Janet had her initial reservations. "I have to be in love," she said, with a twinkling eye. And then added, almost as an afterthought:

"I don't know what Paddy would think."

I laughed.

"The same thing, I'm sure, that he thought when you married Everett."

To the end we both maintained the fiction of Paddy, for he had been a very useful invention and she was loath to give him up.

Prestie's professions of devotion finally disposed of her

doubts. They eloped into Pennsylvania in February 1978, like teenagers, and were married by a justice of the peace. I joined them in Chapala, Mexico, near Guadalajara, not knowing they were married until they gave me the glad news at the airport.

"As you know," Janet explained, "I like being in chains."

After the Mexican honeymoon they stopped off in California. I threw them a small party, but was amazed at the number of uninvited people who swarmed in at the prospect of meeting her. The popularity of *Captains and the Kings* and *Testimony of Two Men* on television had brought her a celebrity rivaling that of any movie star.

As the party proceeded, she sat on her throne chair with the regality of a Cornelia. The partygoers formed an eager circle, dashing off questions about every subject from reincarnation to Women's Lib. She graciously put her answers on their slips of paper so they could have some memento of the occasion. On this particular evening, she once more disclaimed reincarnation, but vaguely acknowledged some form of survival. "Only God," she said, "knows the riddle of His own universe."

As though saluting a peer, the well-known Los Angeles psychic Akashan came forward and took her hand. As he did so, he looked at her closely.

"You are having a legal problem," he said, writing it down when she appeared not to hear.

She looked at him sharply. "I am always having legal problems."

He regarded her sympathetically. "But this concerns a daughter. Is that not true?"

I was hoping that was the end of it, but Akashan showed no sign of moving on.

She had withdrawn her hand and was staring at him uncomfortably.

I wondered if she knew he was a psychic and felt immediately that she must, for she was obviously tuned in to whatever he was thinking.

"I don't know if this makes any sense, but I see a coffin

around you," he went on, adding quickly, "Oh, it's not yours. You've got years ahead of you and lots of things to do. But it could be somebody close, somebody you know." At her expression of dismay he hastily amended his forecast. "It could be the death of old ideas and the birth of a new life."

She turned away with a scowl as her husband came forward helpfully, interrupting this unexpected reading.

Back home, her marriage appeared to prosper, with Prestie taking command of her affairs. There was plenty to handle. *I, Judas* was taken by the book clubs and translated into several languages. In this country the liberal reviewers, with their critical posture of Taylor Caldwell, attributed whatever defects they saw to her. Some reviewers, praising the book extravagantly, termed it one of the most important Christian documents since the New Testament. The book seemed destined for a long run, stirring considerable interest, as well as a theatrical motion picture.

Meanwhile, even as her *Ceremony of the Innocent* slipped from the best-seller lists, it was succeeded by her *Bright Flows the River.* In this book she dealt for the first time with the vagaries of psychiatry. She brought together two friends, one a psychiatrist, the other his patient, and wove their lives with an insight into the human psyche gained from no conscious observations of her own. I remembered now that in her regressions into the medicine of ancient Greece, she had stressed the mind as a factor in illness, just as she had in *Dear and Glorious Physician.*

These two best-sellers had four-word titles, as had all the other best-sellers she had written in the last twenty years. The huge success of *Dear and Glorious Physician*, followed in 1960 by the less successful *The Listener*, undoubtedly influenced every title after that, from *A Prologue to Love* in 1961 on. And who could question her luck symbol, for her twenty years of uninterrupted best-sellers was a publishing record in itself.

Prestie, proud of her contribution, surrounded her with the most amiable working conditions. He was a buffer against the many demands on her time and sought to introduce some regularity into their lives. She would complain at not seeing some of her old friends, the stray males and husbands she liked to entertain, but by and large she was pleased to have somebody with a firm hand arranging things for her.

Janet had been married four times, and Prestie twice, but they were like newlyweds. There was a spanking new Rolls-Royce, new homes in Palm Beach, Florida, and Palm Springs, plans for a townhouse in London, and a country house in Greenwich, Connecticut, and now a dramatic encore to their marriage.

I thought there was nothing she could do to surprise me. But a few months after their marriage I received an excited phone call from Prestie, announcing they were planning to be married in the Catholic Church, and would I be best man.

It struck me as so much window-trimming. But for Janet it would be her first marriage in her own church. Knowing her sense of drama, I could see her smiling at the raised eyebrows in bourgeois Buffalo. What a scene for a book.

Prestie was Catholic, with a teen-age son by his first marriage. The boy now lived with them and she doted on him, never having had a son of her own. She sent him to a Catholic school and marked his progress with pride. When people asked if she had returned to the Church, she stared coldly and said, "I never left it. It is my chief beneficiary."

I was still puzzled, as were others, just how the accommodations had been made for a ceremony in a church which didn't recognize divorce and held marriage eternal.

"How did you manage it?" I asked Prestie.

"Well, it took some doing," he said, "but Janet was never married in the Catholic Church. And so, technically, Janet was never really married in the eyes of the Church."

There would soon be no living ex-husbands to complicate things. Marcus was long dead, as was her first husband, Bill Combs, and Everett, terminally ill, was expected to go at any time. (He died shortly thereafter.)

If she hoped to create a sensation, she succeeded sensationally. The Buffalo newspapers prominently reported the Church wedding. And among the local population, predominantly Catholic, there were complaints that because of her celebrity she was granted special treatment. The Catholic hierarchy calmly maintained that all the proprieties had been met.

The ceremony was small but impressive, attended by a handful of relatives and intimates. I was so busy looking around that I missed my cue and failed to produce the ring at the right moment, but finally, fumblingly, found it. Later, there was a swank reception at which Janet enjoyably presided, taking it all in stride. She seemed to gain new strength from every crisis she fashioned for herself.

As a traditionalist, the Catholic ceremony gave the marriage a new stability in Janet's eyes. It brought her closer to Prestie, giving him a distinction none of her other husbands had. He increasingly took hold of her affairs, including the handling of Judy's claims. The action was complicated by past generosity. Having so freely given Marcus credit for assistance, even to saying he wrote passages he was not capable of writing, she now had to defend the claim that Marcus had contributed significantly to her novels. This, together with her hearing problem and high blood pressure, boded a court fight that could have imposed a dangerous stress. She had no wish to repudiate what she had given Marcus, nor to demean his memory. Prestie prudently sought to resolve the action out of court.

"Can you imagine," she said almost woefully, "poor Marcus writing my books?"

As energetic as ever, she turned to a new project. This was to be a contemporary novel, deriving a special flavor from the Old Testament story of Job, the symbol of man's enduring tribulation and faith in the sight of God.

But the book that still held her was *Mary*. She could not get it out of her mind. She would leaf through the pages she had written, then start up again only to put it away. She waited vainly for lightning to strike. It was three years since I had read the first exciting pages.

She wrote because she was compelled and Mary was her

compulsion. Now, in her zeal to realize this dearest wish, she visited the Holy Land with Prestie in the summer of 1979, hoping to find some familiar site, voice, or artifact that would touch off a flow of memories—or images—comparable to the visual experience in Florence and, again, while she was regressed.

I had suggested additional regressions, but she would not hear of it. "I don't need any props," she said tartly.

The journey to Israel had been interesting, but not especially productive. Meanwhile, she was getting touchy about criticism she would once have disdained and was moved to retort angrily when accused of being a dispenser of "light fiction."

And so countless thousands of Buffalonians were astounded one morning to read this Caldwellian phillipic in their morning newspaper:

"I write political, industrial, business, medical, and historical novels and books about the persecution of minorities in the United States, especially the Irish, German and Negro minorities—and Jewish, too. Also I write about the real causes of war and not what governments tell us.

"My first anti-war novel, *Dynasty of Death*, published in 1938 and still going strong all over the world, raised the screaming wrath of the 'liberals' in the media, accusing me of trying to prevent a Holy War. These are now the very same people who call me a 'warmonger' for trying to enlighten the American people about Communism.

"A famous surgeon at Johns Hopkins Medical School and hundreds of other doctors all over the world wrote in praise of my medical novels and asked me if I were a physician myself. Scholars who specialize in research on Genghis Khan, the Mongol conqueror of China, have written lauding me for that book, which they use in their classes. My book on the great Marcus Cicero, consul of Rome, is used by professors all over the world in their history classes on ancient Rome."

Serious fiction, she concluded, was not only "about housewives, for housewives." It was designed to make people think of the world we live in, and beyond.

Toward the end of that summer there was good news.

The suit with Judy had finally been settled out of court, with Janet giving up a substantial share of the royalties in the Marcus period. The unpleasant matter was now happily done with—or so we thought.

And so on a note of pleasant anticipation I received an invitation to a gala party in Buffalo honoring Janet's seventy-ninth birthday. It was to be held on September 9, two days after her birthday as a child of the century.

The party never took place. Some strange, perverse Fate willed otherwise. The news came like a staggering bolt of lightning. I could not believe it. It seemed incredible, unreal, and unbelievably cruel. Dear, sweet Judy, still estranged from her mother in settlement, had shot and killed herself.

I put down the phone and sat stunned for an indeterminable time, seeing the two of them as I had seen them first, smiling tenderly at one another and holding hands. Whatever the differences, and however they had been sown, I knew that Janet's love was never far from the surface, ready to respond at the slightest overture.

"Poor Judy," I thought, and then thought of Janet and the pangs that must be hers. Even the way the news broke had been incredibly cruel.

She had been at breakfast, leafing through the morning paper when her wandering eye fell on a headline reporting the death. Nobody had prepared her for it. It hit her with staggering force, and a cry of anguish burst from her lips. "My daughter, Judy! No, no, it can't be—she can't be dead!"

It was almost as if we had slipped back two thousand years, and she, Hannah bat Jacob, was witnessing a cruel assault on another daughter—it had been too much for her then, and now, at this instant, I wondered how she would bear up under this latest stroke.

Had she had some premonition, some feeling of foreboding, that day she had uneasily turned away from the psychic Akashan in my home? Had there been anything prophetic in her own writing, anything suggestive in her own regressions, where she was so often a suicide? Tragic passages from *Never Victorious, Never Defeated* swirled about like a bad dream from the past:

"Jon. Why did you die? It wasn't the poison, for there was no poison. Did you die because you couldn't stand what you had made of your life? But you didn't make your life, not entirely. Cornelia helped you, though you never understood. But a death is never simple, not a death like yours. There are a thousand agonies. A man killed himself, and a hundred people are guilty of it; but no one ever punishes them, no one ever cries out to them, 'Cain, where is thy brother, Abel?' Rest in peace, Jon. And if you still live, forgive me."

I understand anew how much the title *Never Victorious, Never Defeated* signified to her. Another woman might have broken. But Janet reached back into her hard core of spirituality. She did not rant or rave, she made no outcries against the Maker. She had seen and written enough of life to know there was little any of us could do about death put pray. She sat silently for hours, sighing, the tears brimming in her eyes. In the end, there was still *Mary* to turn to, to relive in this immaculate story a loss in some ways like her own. Wasn't the Christ story in a way the story of the human condition?

It was not all darkness, not for those who believed there was always a new day, a fresh, bright morning with sparkling dew glistening on the hills and fields as far as the eye could see:

"The first beams of gauzy sunlight suddenly struck the room. Richard stood in the light, and spare as he was, he seemed to acquire stature and a quiet dignity which could never be overthrown. 'The sun will always come up,' he said. 'There will always be the mornings. Who knows? But that generations in the future there will be a new morning always for our grand-children, if not for us? After all, there is always a God.''

So she had written, and so she believed. Years after *Search for a Soul* people still asked whether she now believed in reincarnation. I had never doubted this, for one could not believe in God and believe that He had put us here just to live out some meaningless cycle, dying without ever knowing why we were born. "This search for God," she told me once, "holds the real meaning of life. Without some illuminating awareness of the final revelation, man is little more than an animal, however powerful he appears."

Her own search for God was a quest as well for the meaning of her own life, for if her life held meaning, then all lives had meaning.

For the benefit of others, I hoped to resolve her contradictory posture on reincarnation.

"How can you not believe in it," I said, "when you constantly refer to past-life experiences?"

"Of course I believe," she smiled, "for I have been there and back many times. But I do enjoy being controversial."

In her *Mary*, when she got to it, there would perhaps be some final clue as to the Second Coming and to Armageddon, the Judgment Day she spoke of in a hushed whisper that evening we first met. Until that day, there would be a suspension of the cataclysm portended in the Bible and in her own brooding mind. Of that she was sure.

She had an amazing resilience, born of her faith, and she was brimming with optimism when I saw her next on the *Rotterdam* as it berthed for a few hours in Los Angeles in January of 1980. She was on a world cruise with Prestie and her daughter Peggy. Judy's death still saddened her, and she would stare into space and wipe a vagrant tear from her eye. But then she would pull herself together and brightly discuss her ongoing projects. She had completed the novel with its theme from Job.

After Barker's death, her relationship with Doubleday gradually deteriorated. She had on deposit with Doubleday more than two million dollars in accumulated royalties, not bearing interest because of a deferral agreement signed years before. By this arrangement, which had its tax benefits at the time, she drew out something less than $100,000 a year in past royalties, supplemented, of course, by her whopping advances on new books. When the income tax rate had been scaled down, this seemed manifestly unfair and Prestie pushed for an end to this one-sided arrangement, and payment of the two million. Nelson Doubleday, head of the family-controlled firm, and Neltje's brother, was busily engaged in spending millions to buy a big league baseball team—the New York Mets—and refused to abrogate the old agreement. Consequently in some acrimony, Janet left Doubleday after twenty years, for a two-book deal with Putnam. Her first book with them, with its contemporary theme from Job, had its usual four-word title, *Answer as a Man.* The book was dedicated to her husband, Prestie, who, she wrote, always answered as a man. It soon became a runaway best-seller.

She was a hard learner, and writing this book had been a good lesson. Prestie mentioned she had been offered an advance of $500,000 for the book, but he was sure she could get a million if she wanted it. She shrugged indifferently at this talk of money, and her eyes took on that introspective look that marked her more serious reflections.

"You may recall," she said over the luncheon table, "that years ago I predicted the rise of Islam, and we see it all happening today in Iran [where they then held Americans hostage], Pakistan, Libya, and in the banding together of the OPEC countries to make a weapon of Moslem oil."

She was now shopping her next book around in her mind and would get on with it when the cruise ended.

"Will it be *Mary*?" I asked.

She hesitated, then shook her head.

"No, I am going back to the warrior Saladin and the story of Islam. It would have been so timely had I brought it out at the time Lee Barker wanted it so badly."

"Saladin may be timely," I said, "but the other is eternal."

"It will come," she said, "when it is ready."

I did not doubt this for a moment. For even as I looked at her, the dazzling image of Darios seemed to hover about her, and I could see a mighty procession of planets arching high among the stars.

"Will we all be on Melina one day?" I asked.

"If we are lucky," she said, and her face broke into a radiant smile. "And if the good Lord can stand us."